NORTH CAROLINA
STATE BOARD OF COMMUNITY COLLEGES
LIBRARIES
SAMPSON TECHNICAL COLLEGE

Y0-BCW-556

Fundamentals of Electricity
and
Automotive Electrical Systems

TL
272
W33

Fundamentals of Electricity
and
Automotive Electrical Systems

TOM WEATHERS, JR.

CLAUD C. HUNTER

Chairman, Automotive Department
Central Piedmont Community College

PRENTICE-HALL, INC. *Englewood Cliffs, New Jersey 07632*

Library of Congress Cataloging in Publication Data

Weathers, Tom.
    Fundamentals of electricity and automotive electrical systems.

    Includes index.
    1. Automobiles—Electric equipment.   2. Automobiles—Electric equipment—Maintenance and repair.
I.   Hunter, Claud C., joint author.   II. Title.
TL272.W33   629.2'54   80-19378
ISBN 0-13-337030-5

Editorial production supervision and interior design
   by Barbara A. Cassel
Manufacturing Buyer: Joyce Levatino

©1981 by Prentice-Hall, Inc., Englewood Cliffs, N.J. 07632

All rights reserved. No part of this book
may be reproduced in any form or
by any means without permission in writing
from the publisher.

Printed in the United States of America

10   9   8   7   6   5   4   3   2   1

PRENTICE-HALL INTERNATIONAL, INC., *London*
PRENTICE-HALL OF AUSTRALIA PTY. LIMITED, *Sydney*
PRENTICE-HALL OF CANADA, LTD., *Toronto*
PRENTICE-HALL OF INDIA PRIVATE LIMITED, *New Delhi*
PRENTICE-HALL OF JAPAN, INC., *Tokyo*
PRENTICE-HALL OF SOUTHEAST ASIA PTE. LTD., *Singapore*
WHITEHALL BOOKS LIMITED, *Wellington, New Zealand*

Contents

Preface

The electrical aspect of modern automobile operation is generally considered to be the most difficult to understand. It involves concepts not often used and operations that cannot be seen, only imagined. Yet to work on cars, you need to know something about electricity. More and more automotive functions that were once performed mechanically are now done with electrical devices.

The actual physical work a mechanic must do in electrical testing or repair is not too difficult. The problem is understanding what to do and why it is done. That is what this book is about. It is intended to give you a grounding in the basic electrical concepts and operations you need to do electrical work. The book won't make you an expert; you'll need to read additional books and get your hands dirty more than once for that. However, the book will hopefully help bring you to the point where you can approach more detailed shop manuals and workbooks with the information you need to understand them.

The book covers three major areas:

Review of basic engine operation

Electrical theory and engine electrical systems

Service sampler

The electricity fundamentals section makes up the majority of the book and is the most important part. The brief review pages are for beginning students who might need additional background information before getting into the electrical chapters (or for anyone who may not have thought about the basics in a long time). The service sampler at the end of the book is primarily intended to give a practical flavor to the otherwise abstract and theoretical material. Although the service samplers included are useful, they are by no means a complete guide for servicing electrical systems. Complete testing and service information is best obtained from shop manuals or specialty books devoted to that subject.

You'll note as you read the book that review questions have been included at frequent intervals. These questions are provided for your benefit to help you fix important facts into your mind. Be sure to answer all of them as you go, checking back into the preceding text when you are not sure of the answer. That way your knowledge will accumulate in a building-block manner, one fact securely lodged in the next.

Tom Weathers, Jr. / Claud C. Hunter

Review of Basic Engine Operation

BASIC ENGINE SYSTEMS

INTRODUCTION The fundamental purpose of the automobile is to move people or things from one place to another. This is done by releasing the stored energy in gasoline. When the gasoline is burned in an engine, its stored energy is converted into mechanical force, which is then transmitted from the engine to the transmission, the driveshaft, the differential, and finally to the driving wheels.

Almost all the basic engine systems relate in one way or another to releasing the stored energy of fuel and controlling it once it is released. This section reviews those basic engine systems.

1. *What is the basic purpose of the automobile?*
2. *How is this purpose accomplished?*

FUEL SYSTEM The fuel system has three basic functions: (1) *storing* fuel until it is needed, (2) *pumping* it from the storage place to the engine, and (3) *mixing* fuel with air so that it can be burned and its energy released.

Fuel is stored in the fuel tank (Fig. 1), a sheet-metal container usually located at the rear of the car between the frame rails.

Fuel is pumped from the tank to the engine by the fuel pump (Fig 1). There are two basic kinds of fuel pumps, mechanical and electrical. *Mechanical pumps* are driven directly by the engine and are attached to the engine itself. *Electrical pumps* may be located anywhere along the fuel line from the tank to the engine. However, they are usually found in the engine compartment or inside the fuel tank.

From the pump, the fuel goes to the carburetor (Fig. 1), which is attached to the top or one side of the engine. The carburetor mixes air with gasoline so that it can be burned and its stored energy released. Fuel is broken into tiny droplets which are combined in different mixtures with air for different operating conditions—starting, idling, normal running, acceleration, and so on.

1.   *What are three functions of fuel systems?*
2.   *What are two basic kinds of fuel pumps?*
3.   *What does the carburetor mix together, and why?*

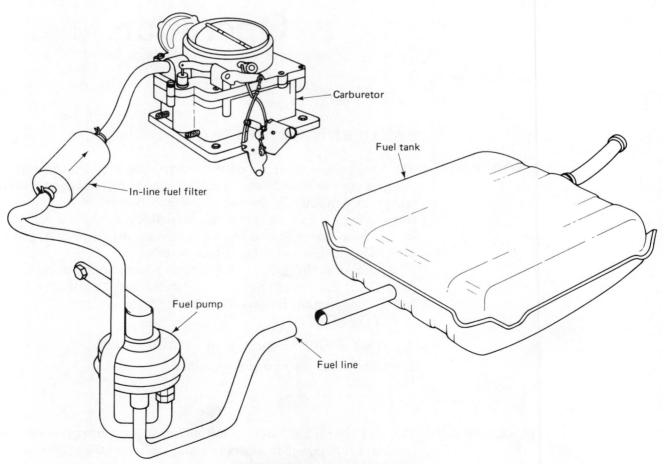

FIG. 1 Fuel system components.

MAIN MECHANICAL SYSTEMS

After the fuel and air have been combined in the carburetor, the mixture goes inside the engine, where it is ignited by a spark plug. Following is a description of the path taken by the fuel.

1. From the carburetor, the mixture goes to the intake manifold (Fig. 2). The *intake manifold* is a large metal casting with holes or passages inside. The carburetor usually sits on top or to one side and delivers the mixture to the manifold passageways.

2. After the intake manifold, the mixture flows through similar passages in the *head*, another large metal casting. The head forms one part of the combustion chamber (the place where the fuel is burned). It contains the spark plugs and the valves used to control the passage of the air/fuel mixture and the exhaust gases.

3. The mixture comes out of the head into the cylinders. The *cylinders* are simply holes in the block, the main part of the engine. The head closes off the top part of the cylinders. The bottom part is closed off by the pistons, which slide up and down inside the cylinders.

4. The space bounded by the head, piston, and cylinder is called the *combustion chamber*. As the piston slides up in the cylinder, the size of the combustion chamber is decreased, thereby "squeezing" the air/fuel mixture trapped inside. When the air/fuel mixture is squeezed tight, it can be more easily ignited by the spark plug, whose tip projects into the combustion chamber.

5. After the mixture has been ignited, a wavefront of flame spreads throughout the combustion chamber. This converts the air-fuel mixture into hot, expanding gas which pushes down on the top of the *piston* with a great deal of force (Fig. 3). The piston is connected by a connecting rod to the *crankshaft*, so that the downward move-

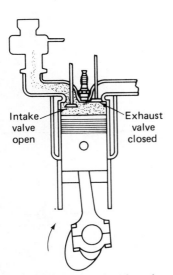

FIG. 2 Intake stroke showing the air/fuel mixture drawn into the cylinder.

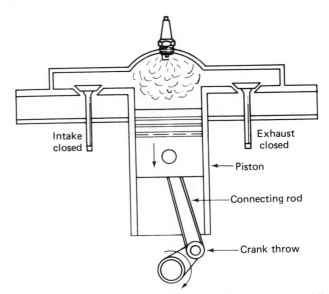

FIG. 3 The ignited air/fuel mixture burns very rapidly, pushing down on the piston head with great force. The connecting rod acting with the crank throw changes the downward motion into rotary motion, which is transmitted to the rear wheels by way of the clutch, transmission drive line, and differential assembly.

ment of the piston is converted into rotational force at the crankshaft. This rotational force is transmitted to the transmission, drive shaft, differential, and driving wheels.

1. *Describe the flow path of the air/fuel mixture from the carburetor to the combustion chamber.*
2. *What parts make up the combustion chamber?*
3. *What causes the crankshaft to rotate?*

IGNITION SYSTEMS Two conditions are necessary to release the stored energy in fuel: (1) it must be mixed with air in the correct amount to burn, and (2) a spark must be present to ignite the fuel mixture.

The *spark plug* is the heart of the ignition system [Fig. 4(a)]. When electricity flows to the spark plug, an arc jumps between the electrodes at the tip. This arc (which is timed to take place just as the piston moves into the proper position in the combustion chamber) begins the burning process in the air/fuel mixture.

Electricity for the spark plug originates at the battery. However, the battery voltage by itself is not great enough to create the spark. The voltage must be increased or stepped up. That is the job of the

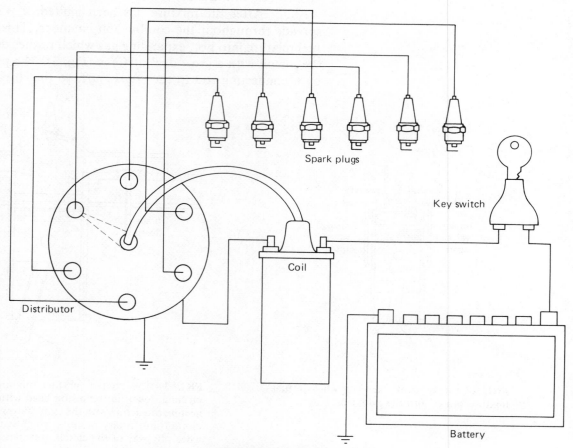

Spark plugs

Key switch

Coil

Distributor

Battery

FIG. 4 Basic ignition system.

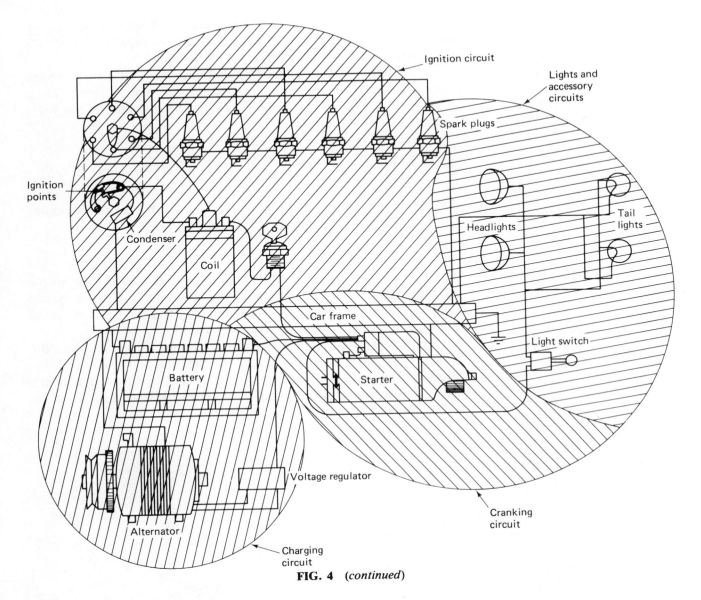

FIG. 4 (*continued*)

ignition coil. It takes the low voltage and increases it to around 15,000 to 20,000 volts. This is enough energy to produce an arc at the spark plug tip.

The high-voltage surge from the coil is triggered by certain components in the *distributor*. These components act as the "brain" of the ignition system, telling the coil when to discharge. This must happen at precise times so that energy reaches the spark plug at the instant it is needed.

Besides triggering the high-voltage surge from the coil, the distributor has another job. It must route or send the high-voltage surge to the particular spark plug that is ready to fire at that moment. As its name suggests, the distributor "distributes" electricity to the spark plugs.

The entire ignition system may be divided into two main groups of parts [Fig. 4(b)]. The parts of the system that carry low-voltage, battery current are called the *primary circuit*. They include the battery itself, the ignition switch, the low-voltage parts of the distributor, and the low-voltage side of the coil.

The parts of the ignition system that carry the high-voltage surge produced by the coil are called the *secondary circuit*. These parts include the "distributing" part of the distributor, the high-voltage side of the coil, and the spark plug.

1. *Where is battery voltage converted into a high-voltage surge?*
2. *What are the two main functions of the distributor?*
3. *Name the parts of the primary and secondary ignition circuits.*
4. *Which circuit carries higher voltage?*

EXHAUST SYSTEM The fuel and ignition systems work together to convert the stored energy of fuel into power to operate the automobile. The fuel system delivers the fuel and prepares it for burning and the ignition system provides the spark to set off the combustion process.

However, the fuel is not totally consumed during combustion. Some fuel is not burned at all. And the fuel that is burned yields byproducts: exhaust gases, water, solid particles, and heat. The heat is dissipated by the cooling system. The exhaust system disposes of the other waste.

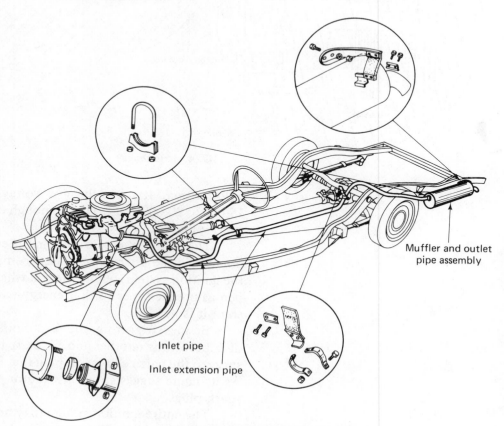

Muffler and outlet
pipe assembly

Inlet pipe

Inlet extension pipe

FIG. 5 Typical exhaust system.

Following is a brief discussion of how the exhaust system works (Fig. 5):

First, the unburned fuel and exhaust by-products are pushed through the open exhaust valve by the piston as it goes up in the cylinder. From there the exhaust goes through passages in the head to the *exhaust manifold* (a collection of pipes attached to the head). Then the exhaust passes through an exhaust pipe to the *muffler*. The muffler quiets the noise of the combustion process. Finally, the exhaust is vented into the atmosphere through the *tail pipe*.

In years past, the exhaust was dumped raw into the air. However, since the polluting effects of automobile exhaust reached a danger level in the mid-1960s, the exhaust system has been controlled.

1. *Is fuel totally consumed in the burning process?*
2. *What is contained in exhaust coming out of the tail pipe?*
3. *Trace the exhaust flow path.*

ELECTRICAL SYSTEM There are two sources of stored energy in an automobile (aside from the driver). One source is gasoline. It supplies the chemical energy to operate the engine. The other source is the *battery*. It provides the electrical energy to operate the spark plugs, which, in turn, release the stored energy in the gasoline. The battery also supplies the electrical power for the lights, horn, radio, starter motor, and so on [Fig. 6(a)].

The battery is the heart of the electrical system. All other parts of the electrical systems fall into two main groups [Fig. 6(b)]: (1) components that *use* the battery's electricity, and (2) components that *resupply* the battery's energy loss.

The first group of components, those that *use* electricity, include the starter motor, horn, radio, ignition system, and accessories.

The other group of components are all included in the *charging system*. The heart of the charging system is the *alternator* (or in older cars, the generator). The alternator (or generator) is driven by a pulley-and-belt assembly connected to the engine's crankshaft. In effect, the charging system takes some of the power used to drive the engine and converts it into electrical energy to resupply the energy lost by the battery. As long as the engine is running, the alternator pumps electrical energy back into the battery roughly equal to the amount it loses. (Although you should be aware that at certain times, both the battery and the alternator supply electrical energy to the car.)

1. *What is the second source of stored energy in a car (aside from the driver)?*
2. *Name the two main groups of the electrical system and some of the parts included in each.*
3. *What is the heart of the electrical system?*

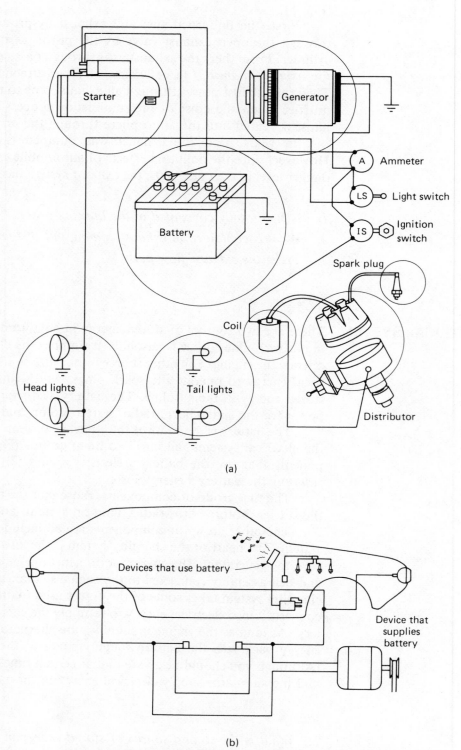

(a)

(b)

FIG. 6 All these devices remove energy from the battery under some operating conditions. The only exception is the generator; it uses energy from the engine to recharge the battery.

LUBRICATING SYSTEM   The inside of the internal combustion engine is a hostile environment for the precision parts that must work there. Heat and contamination are produced by the combustion process, and friction is created by parts in sliding contact with one another. If it were not for the lubricating oils, the engine could not operate (Fig. 7).

Engine lubricating oils serve three main functions. First, oil helps to remove some of the excess heat from the engine. It acts as a heat-transfer medium. Second, the oil flushes away contaminants and debris from critical operating areas. It acts as a cleaning agent. The third and primary function of lubricating oil is to form a protective film between surfaces that are in sliding contact, such as the piston and cylinder walls, and the crankshaft and crankshaft bearings. The oil is a lubricant that reduces friction and wear.

Oil is usually stored in the oil pan at the bottom of the engine. (See Fig. 7.) From there it is pumped through channels to different parts of the engine. Because the oil picks up waste and debris on its way through the engine, a filter must be employed. In older engines, the oil was filtered just before returning to the oil pan. Newer engines usually strain the oil just after it leaves the pan.

1.   What are the three main functions of lubricating oils in the engine?

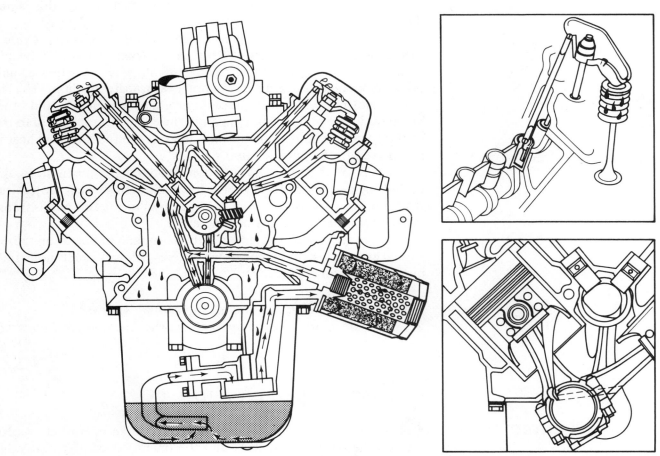

FIG. 7   Lubrication system.

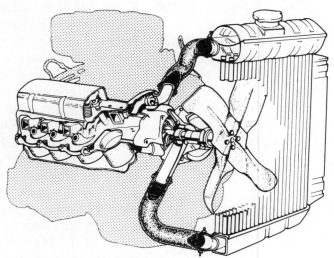

FIG. 8 Cooling system.

COOLING SYSTEM   The combustion process is not 100% perfect. If it were, all the stored energy in fuel would be converted into force to drive the car. There would be no need for an exhaust system to get rid of solid and gaseous waste. And a cooling system wouldn't be required because the engine would produce no waste heat. Unfortunately, this is not the case, and both exhaust and cooling systems are required.

The basic function of the *cooling system* (Fig. 8) is to provide a way to take waste heat from the engine and transfer it to the outside atmosphere. A liquid coolant made up of water, antifreeze, and other components is the most common heat-transfer medium. The liquid coolant is circulated in passages around the cylinders and other hot areas in the engine. The heat from the engine is transferred to the coolant, and then, after the coolant goes to the radiator, the heat is transferred to the outside atmosphere.

Air is another, but less common, heat-transfer medium. In air-cooled engines, air is blown over metal cooling fins which project out from the hot parts of the engine. Heat flows to the fins and is transferred from the fins to the cooling air.

There are few air-cooled automobile engines in operation today. Primarily, the system is limited to motorcycles and small industrial, home, and farm engines.

1. *What is the main function of the cooling system?*
2. *What is the most common heat-transfer medium used in cars?*

FOUR-STROKE OPERATION

INTRODUCTION   This section reviews the principle of four-stroke operation. It also reviews the basic components and the operation of a typical valve train. And it identifies the terms TDC, BDC, BTCD, and ATDC.

FOUR-STROKE OPERATION

The basic steps in the operation of a four-stroke engine are (1) moving the air and fuel into the cylinders, (2) compressing the fuel mixture so that it will burn efficiently, (3) burning the mixture and thereby extracting the stored energy from the fuel, and (4) removing the exhaust gases from the cylinder after the fuel has been burned. To complete these steps, the engine must go through four strokes of the piston.

First is the *intake stroke*, when the piston moves down in the cylinder (Fig. 9). As it moves down, a region of lower air pressure is created in the vacant space over the piston. The higher atmospheric pressure in the carburetor pushes the air/fuel mixture from the carburetor through the intake manifold and head into the cylinder.

Second is the *compression stroke* (Fig. 10), when the piston moves back up in the cylinder. This action squeezes the air and fuel into a dense, combustible mixture at the top of the cylinder. Compressing the air/fuel mixture makes it easier to release its stored power.

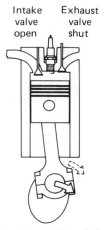

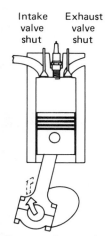

FIG. 9   Intake stroke of the piston during one four-stroke cycle.

FIG. 10   Compression stroke of the piston during the four-stroke cycle.

Note: The amount the air–fuel mixture is squeezed is determined by the *compression ratio* (the ratio between the volume or space in the cylinder when the piston is at the top of its stroke and when it is at the bottom; see Fig. 11). For instance, if there are 50 cubic inches in

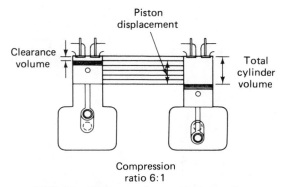

FIG. 11   Diagram of compression ratio.

the cylinder when the piston is at the bottom of its stroke and 5 cubic inches when the piston is at the top, the compression ratio will be 10:1. In other words, the volume in the cylinder is 10 times as great as when the cylinder is at the bottom of its stroke than when it is at the top.

Next comes the *power stroke* (Fig. 12), when the stored energy in the fuel is converted into power to operate the engine. The power stroke begins just before, just as, or just after the compression stroke is ending, when the piston is near the top of its travel in the cylinder. First the spark plug fires. Then the air/fuel mixture ignites, spreading a wavefront of flame and hot gases through the densely packed air/fuel mixture. The expanding gases push down on the top of the piston with a great deal of force. This force (transmitted to the crankshaft by the piston rod) operates the engine and moves the vehicle.

The fourth and final step in the operating cycle is the *exhaust stroke* (Fig. 13). This occurs when the piston comes back up in the cylinder to push the exhaust gases and waste from the cylinder.

FIG. 12   Power stroke of the piston during one four-stroke cycle.

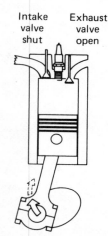

FIG. 13   Exhaust stroke of the piston during one four-stroke cycle.

In summary, the four steps in the operation of a four-stroke engine are: (1) the intake stroke, when the piston goes down to draw the air/fuel mixture into the cylinder; (2) the compression stroke, when the piston goes up to compress the air and fuel into a dense, combustible mixture; (3) the power stroke, when the fuel mixture burns to push the piston down in the cylinder; and (4) the exhaust stroke, when the piston goes back up to push the exhaust gases from the cylinder.

Note: Only the power stroke is responsible for piston movement. The other three up-and-down strokes of the piston are due to the momentum created (and then stored in the flywheel) by the downward thrust of the piston in the power stroke. Enough rotational energy is given to the crankshaft assembly during the power stroke to move the piston up and down three more times for the other strokes, plus providing enough energy to drive the automobile.

1. *Name the four strokes of a four-stroke engine and tell which direction the piston is moving in each stroke.*
2. *Which is the only stroke that actually causes the piston to move?*

VALVE TRAIN How does the air/fuel mixture get into the cylinders during the intake stroke, and how are the exhaust gases removed during the exhaust stroke? The answer is the *valve train*. Intake ports and intake valves admit the fuel mixture into the cylinders. Exhaust valves and ports remove the exhaust gases.

During the intake stroke, the intake valve is opened and the exhaust valve closed (Fig. 14). The open intake valve allows the air/fuel mixture to be drawn through the intake port as the piston goes down in the cylinder. Then during the compression and power strokes, both valves are closed and the combustion chamber thereby sealed off (Fig. 15). For the final, exhaust stroke, the exhaust valve is opened and the intake valve is closed. The open exhaust valve allows the exhaust gases to be pushed through the exhaust port and on into the exhaust manifold.

The operation of the valves—their opening and closing—is controlled by the *camshaft*. The camshaft is a long rod, driven by the crankshaft and usually located in the block or the head. It has a number of lobes, or cam surfaces along its length, one lobe for each valve.

The camshaft and the crankshaft are connected by a timing chain which runs on sprockets at the ends of each shaft. The camshaft sprocket has twice as many teeth as the crankshaft sprocket,

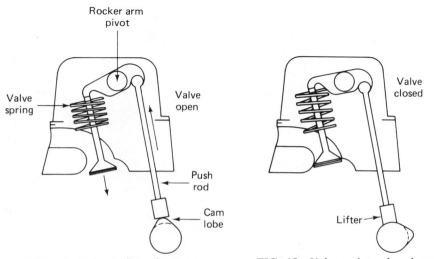

FIG. 14 Valve train: valve open.   **FIG. 15** Valve train: valve closed.

which means that the camshaft rotates half as fast as the crankshaft, causing the valves to open and close once for every two crankshaft revolutions. Proper valve opening and closing is related to this basic fact of engine design, as well as to the relative position of the crankshaft and the camshaft.

1.   *When are the intake and exhaust valves opened and closed? During which operating strokes?*
2.   *Name the basic components of the valve train.*

PISTON-POSITION TERMS   The time the valves open and close is one aspect of engine timing. Another is the timing of the spark plug's firing. The spark plugs must fire when the piston is at a particular position, either just before, just as, or just after the compression stroke ends. Following are the shorthand terms mechanics use to refer to the position of a piston in a cylinder, whether it is up or down (Fig. 16).

First is TDC. It means *top dead center*, when the piston is at the top of its travel in the cylinder. Second is BDC, or *bottom dead center*. This is when the piston is at the bottom of its travel in the

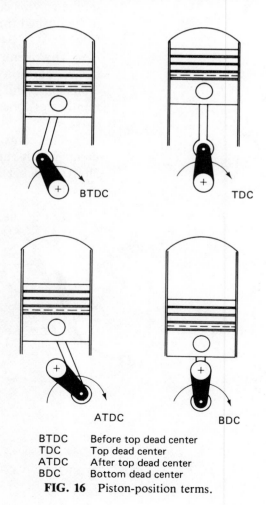

BTDC	Before top dead center
TDC	Top dead center
ATDC	After top dead center
BDC	Bottom dead center

FIG. 16 Piston-position terms.

cylinder. BTDC, or *before top dead center*, means the piston has not quite reached the top of its travel in the cylinder. And ATDC, or *after top dead center* means the piston has just gone by TDC and is traveling back down in the cylinder again.

As the piston moves reciprocally up and down, the crankshaft is moving in a circular manner. Therefore, these piston position terms also relate to the position of the crankshaft—usually measured in degrees of rotation. For example, the term TDC also means zero degrees TDC, because when the piston is at top dead center, the crankshaft is said not have not rotated. Or, after the piston starts back down and the crankshaft has rotated 5 or 10 degrees, the piston is said to be at 5 or 10 degrees ATDC. And, if the crankshaft only has to rotate 6 degrees before the piston reaches TDC, the piston is said to be at 6 degrees BTDC.

1. *What do the terms "TDC," "BDC," and "ATDC" mean?*
2. *If the crankshaft rotates 10 degrees after the piston is at TDC, is the piston at 10 degrees ADTC or 10 degrees BTDC?*

section

1

Electrical Theory
and
Engine Electrical Systems

chapter

1

Atomic Theory, Volts, Amps, and Ohms

INTRODUCTION
To understand electricity and the way it works in automobiles, you need to know something about the concept of electricity itself, something about the basic nature of matter, and something about the fundamental ways in which electricity is described. This chapter provides these elemental facts. It also introduces the concept of current flow.

ELECTRICITY—NO-THING
No one really knows what electricity is, because electricity is not exactly a *thing*. It is not something you can put your hands on. Sometimes you can feel its effects if you accidentally touch a charged wire. But the wire (a *thing*) is not electricity. The charged wire has some extra quality not possessed by the uncharged wire.

Since electricity is *no-thing*, the best way to understand it is to compare it with *some-thing*. Over the years the "something" most often compared with electricity is water.

So, first of all, think about an electrical wire (or any carrier of electricity) as behaving like water. Then imagine that the water is dammed up in a man-made lake. There is water in the lake above the dam and water in the stream below. The water, like the electrical wire is definitely a thing; you can see it and touch it.

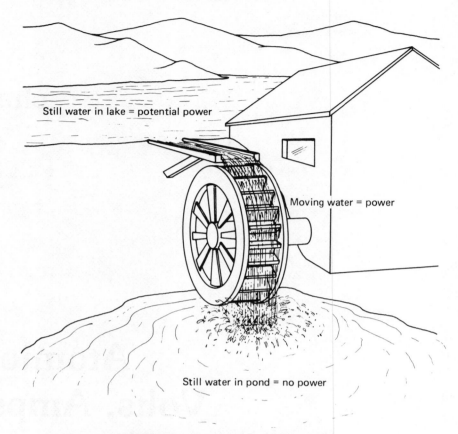

Still water in lake = potential power

Moving water = power

Still water in pond = no power

FIG. 1-1   The force of moving water.

Now suppose that the lake is used to operate a mill (Fig. 1-1). Under the influence of gravity, water flows down through pipes and passages until it comes to the waterwheel, where its force is used to operate the mill.

What happens to the water as it goes down from the dam? It remains water. It is still a *thing*. But for a time, it also has an extra quality. As it flows down through the dam it has acquired movement and force. While it is moving, it is something more than the quiet, still water above the dam.

To visualize this extra quality in another way, imagine that you are holding your left hand in a sink full of still water and that you are holding your right hand under a faucet turned on full force. No effort is required to keep your left hand stationary. But considerable effort is needed to hold your right hand against the force of the open faucet.

In both these examples you are touching water. However, the running water has an "extra quality." It is not a thing; you can't see it or taste it. You can't really touch it either, although you can feel its effects.

Electricity acts in somewhat the same way (Fig. 1-2). When you pick up an ordinary piece of bare copper wire, nothing happens. Yet should you attach the same piece of wire to a 110 volt outlet you would receive a shock (perhaps fatal). The wire has not changed. It is

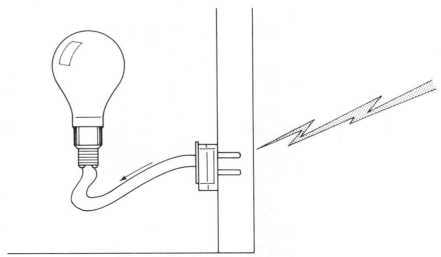

FIG. 1-2 Electricity is movement and power.

still copper. However, when it is attached to the outlet it acquires an extra quality, just as water under the influence of gravity acquires an extra quality. The extra quality given to water is movement and force. The same kind of extra quality is given to the wire when it is plugged into the outlet. The shock you receive is an indication of the force of this movement, just as the arc across a spark plug's gap is a visible sign of electrical pressure and movement.

1. *Is electricity a thing?*
2. *What does a charged wire have that an uncharged wire does not have?*
3. *What does moving water have that still water does not?*
4. *What is the extra quality given to the wire by the 110-volt outlet?*
5. *The arc across a spark plug tip is a visible sign of what?*

ATOMS If electricity is movement, then what moves? When you attach the copper wire to the outlet, you do not see anything move. It is as if you are watching a fast-moving stream with no ripples or waves to give you any sign of the flow.

The reason you don't see any movement is because it takes place in the very smallest parts of the wire. These small parts are called *atoms* (Fig. 1-3). Although atoms themselves don't move, you need to know something about them in order to understand electrical flow. The next several pages will discuss atoms. Then you will see how electrical movement takes place.

All material in the universe—the copper wire, this book, and you yourself—are made up of atoms. Atoms are often referred to as the building blocks of nature.

There are something over 100 kinds of atoms. They are combined in various ways to form larger particles called *molecules*. Molecules

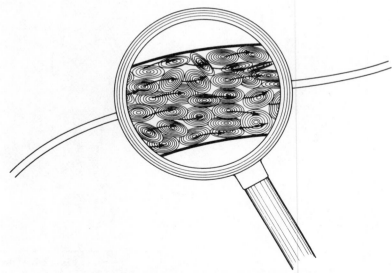

FIG. 1-3 The wire is composed of atoms. Electricity is movement between atoms.

are further combined to form everything there is—solids, liquids, and gases (like air).

No one has ever seen an atom, just its effects. Some scientists even question if atoms can properly be called particles. They say atoms are more like mysterious little moving waves of energy in space. However, for your purposes you can think of atoms as tiny bits of matter.

To get an idea of the size of atoms, a drop of water contains about 100 billion billion of them.

1.   *Where does electrical movement take place?*
2.   *What are the building blocks of nature?*
3.   *What are atoms joined together to form?*
4.   *How many atoms are in a drop of water?*

ELECTRONS AND PROTONS   Even as small as atoms are, they are made up of even smaller particles. The two basic parts of an atom that you need to know about are protons and electrons (Fig. 1-4).

Protons are located at the center, or nucleus, of atoms. *Electrons* are located on the outside. Most atoms have an equal number of protons and electrons, the number depending on the size of the particular atom. Atoms of copper have 29 protons and 29 electrons. Hydrogen, a very light substance that is a gas at normal room temperature, has only 1 electron and 1 proton.

The protons at the center of atoms are more or less stationary. However, the electrons on the outside are always moving. They travel in circular paths called orbits around the center of the atom (actually, three-dimensional energy "shells"). Some electrons move in orbits

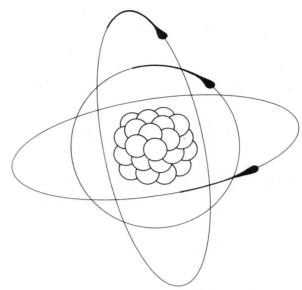

FIG. 1-4 Protons occupy the center or nucleus of atoms. Electrons circle the nucleus in paths called orbits.

near the center or nucleus. Some move in orbits farther away. It is like the solar system with the sun in the center and the planets moving in orbits around the sun. In an atomic structure, the nucleus would be the sun and the electrons planets.

No one knows exactly why electrons move in this way. However, scientists do know that electrons move faster or slower, depending on the temperature. If you could look inside an iron piston in an engine, you would see that the iron atom's electrons move faster when the engine is hot than when it is cold.

Scientists also know why electrons don't fly out of their orbits. (Electrons have a tendency to leave their orbits due to centrifugal force—the same force that throws you against a car's door when you go around a curve.) The restraint that keeps electrons in their orbits is an attraction between electrons and protons.

An electron behaves like the south end of a magnet; it has a negative charge. And a proton acts like the north end of a magnet; it has a positive charge. These opposite charges attract one another, trying to come together.

Therefore, electrons do not fly out of their orbits because they are attracted toward the center of atoms by positively charged protons. A balance is achieved between centrifugal force and magnetic attraction.

1.   *What are the two basic parts of an atom?*

2.   *Where are protons located?*

3.   *Where are electrons located?*

4.   *What do you call the circular path in which electrons travel?*

5. *What happens to the electrons in a piston when the piston be-comes hot?*

6. *Why do electrons have a tendency to leave their orbits?*

7. *What restraint keeps them in their orbits?*

8. *An electron is like which end of a magnet?*

9. *What kind of charge does an electron have?*

10. *What kind of charge does a proton have?*

ELECTRON FLOW In spite of the attraction between electrons and protons, electrons can leave their orbits. An outside force can overcome the attraction between protons and electrons, causing the electrons to move from one atom to another. It is something like the force of gravity upsetting the balance of water behind the dam and causing it to flow to the river below.

This is how electron flow works:

First, imagine a copper wire with a string of atoms running along its length (Fig. 1-5). Then imagine that the ends of the wire are attached to the positive and negative poles of an automotive battery (an outside source of energy, or electromotive force, as it is sometimes called).

The battery's positive terminal (which acts like the south end of a magnet) has a strong attraction for the negatively charged electrons in the copper wire. This attraction is greater than the attraction between the electrons and protons in the copper atoms. Therefore, the

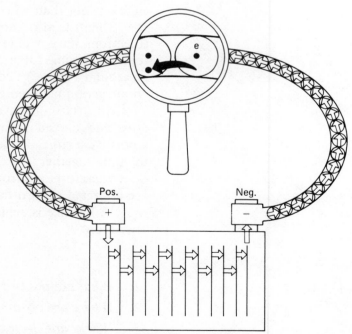

FIG. 1-5 Electrons are drawn out of the wire at the positive pole and pushed into the wire at the negative pole. This chain reaction movement is called current flow.

battery pulls an electron from the outside orbit of the copper atom nearest it.

That atom now has one more proton than electron. In their normal state, atoms have an equal number of electrons and protons and by losing an electron, the atom will have an extra proton. Because of the extra proton, the atom is no longer electrically balanced. The total of all the positive and negative charges is unequal, so the atom has an overall positive charge. Atoms with an overall electrical charge are unstable and will try to balance themselves.

The only convenient way for the atom to balance itself is to gain another electron. And that is what it does—with its overall positive charge (and aided by the pull of the battery's positive pole) it attracts a negatively charged electron from a neighbor atom.

However, on losing an electron, the second atom also becomes unbalanced. And to balance itself, it pulls an electron from the next atom, which, in turn, takes an electron from the next atom, and so on. The chain reaction continues along the wire to the negative pole of the battery. The negative pole pushes electrons into the wire to re-supply those being pulled out the other end by the positive terminal.

This is *electrical flow.* It is the act of the battery (or any other source of electromotive force) pulling electrons out of one end of the wire and pushing electrons into the other end. The energy source "pulls" electrons toward its positive terminal and "pushes" electrons from its negative terminal, creating a continuous flow of electrons through the entire circuit (or electrical path).

1.   *A battery's positive terminal is like which end of a magnet?*

2.   *What part of an atom does the positive terminal attract?*

3.   *What happens when an atom loses an electron?*

4.   *How does the atom balance itself?*

5.   *Where does the atom get the electron to balance itself?*

6.   *What does the neighbor atom do when it loses an electron?*

7.   *What does the next atom do when it loses an electron?*

8.   *Where does the reaction eventually end up?*

9.   *Which pole of the battery pulls electrons from the wire?*

10.   *Which pole pushes electrons into the wire?*

11.   *What do you call the act of pulling electrons out of one end of a wire and pushing them into the other end?*

12.   *In this section, one source of electrical energy was described as pulling and pushing electrons. What source is that?*

**HOW ELECTRICITY
CAUSES WORK
TO BE DONE**

Now that you know how electricity flows, several other questions come to mind. One is: How does electrical flow cause work to be done, in an automobile or any other place?

Although the question will not be answered completely until later chapters, some hints can be given now.

To perform certain jobs, electricity acts on materials directly like water acts on the blades of a water wheel. For instance, the movement of electrons in particular kinds of wires (such as tungsten wire) causes lights to shine—headlamps, tail lights, instrument panel lights, and so on. In like manner, work is done directly when an arc occurs at a spark plug gap. This can be imagined as electrons being pushed past a barrier (the spark plug's air gap) in the path of the electron flow.

Electrical work is also done indirectly, as in the operation of the starter motor or ignition coil. These devices depend on the effect that electron flow has on the space surrounding the material through which the flow takes place.

Electrical flow through certain ferrous metals will create a "field" or area of magnetic force around the material (Fig. 1-6). This field, depending on the circumstances, will cause the material itself, or other, nearby materials to act like magnets with north and south poles. Physical work is done when these "electromagnets" attract and repel one another or other materials. This is how electric motors operate.

Electromagnetic fields can also be manipulated to increase the pressure given an electrical flow. This is how the ignition coil works.

1. Electricity performs work in two basic ways. What are they?

2. Give two examples where electricity works directly.

3. Give two examples where electricity works indirectly.

4. What do you call the effect created around certain materials when electricity flows through them?

5. This effect causes the materials to act like what?

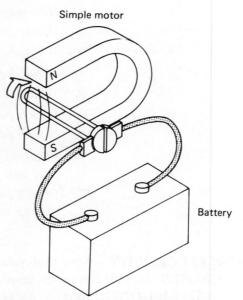

Simple motor

Battery

FIG. 1-6 As current from the battery passes through the wire loop, the lines of force from the loop and the magnet interact, causing the loop to rotate.

ENERGY SOURCES   Another question is: What causes electrons to flow—where does the "pressure" come from?

Basically, there are two sources of electrical pressure or energy in an automobile. One is the alternator or generator. The other is the battery.

Both types of energy sources will be described in the next few chapters. It is sufficient for the moment to note that alternators, like electric motors, make use of magnetic fields (Fig. 1-7). Electrical pressure and flow are created when loops of wire are passed through a magnetic field (or vice versa, when the field moves and the wires remain stationary).

Simple generator

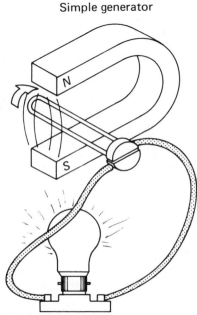

FIG. 1-7 Electrical voltage is created when the wire loop rotates within the magnetic field. Voltage "induced" in this manner causes current to flow through the attached wires and lightbulb.

Batteries, on the other hand, create electrical pressure and flow by chemical means. In automotive batteries, a sulfuric acid "electrolyte" reacts chemically with porous lead "plates." Electrons are put in motion between the plates and the electrodes at the ends of each "cell." This creates a reduction of electrons at one end of the battery and an abundance at the other, causing electron flow in any attached wire, or source of free electrons.

1. *What are the two sources of electrical pressure or energy in an automobile?*

2. *Alternators, like electric motors, make use of what principle in their operation?*

3. *What means do batteries use to create electrical pressure and flow?*

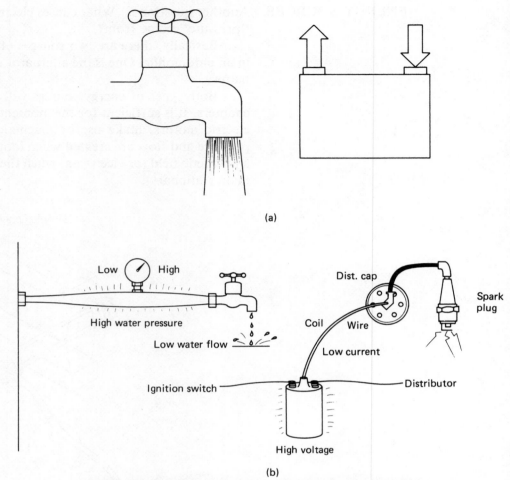

FIG. 1-8   (a) Water pressure is similar to voltage or electrical "push." (b) Voltage versus water pressure.

VOLTS   Various terms are used to describe electrical pressure, quantity, and resistance.

Electrical pressure is called *voltage.* Again, comparing electricity to water, it is like the pressure produced by a water pump (Fig. 1-8).

Each cell in a lead cell battery produces a little over 2 volts (V) of electrical pressure. Therefore, a three-cell battery of the kind used in older model cars provides 6 V of total electrical pressure.

1.   *What term is used to describe electrical pressure?*
2.   *How much electrical pressure do three- and six-cell automotive batteries produce?*

AMPERES   *Amperes* (or amperage or amps) is a term used to describe the quantity of electrical flow—actually the amount of electrons flowing past a given point in a given period of time. It's like the "gallons per minute" produced by the pressure of a water pump (Fig. 1-9).

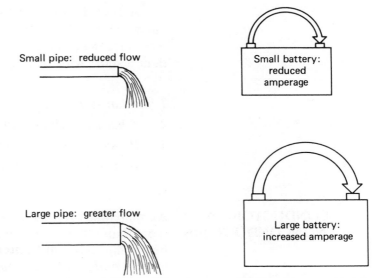

FIG. 1-9 Amperage measures electrical flow in the same way that gallons per minute measures water flow.

An average 12-V automotive battery will delivery 50 amperes (A) for 1 hour (or 100 A for 30 minutes, or 200 A for 15 minutes, and so on).

1. What terms are used to describe the quantity of electrical flow?

OHMS The term *ohm* refers to the amount of resistance in an electrical circuit. Electrical resistance can be compared to the resistance to water flow caused by an obstruction or restriction in a water pipe, (Fig. 1-10).

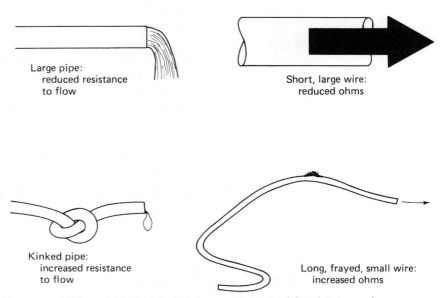

FIG. 1-10 Electrical resistance (measured in ohms) can be compared to resistance in water flow.

A frayed wire or a loose connection will cause electrical resistance. Also, a small-diameter wire, like a small pipe, will have more resistance than a large wire. And a long wire will have more resistance than a short wire. A long wire causes electrons to travel farther.

1. *What term is used to describe electrical resistance?*

2. *What two things cause electrical resistance?*

3. *Which has more resistance, a small- or a large-diameter wire?*

4. *Which has more resistance, a long or a short wire?*

CONDUCTORS AND NONCONDUCTORS

All materials offer some resistance to electrical flow, some materials more than others. It depends in part on how easily their electrons can be put into motion. Materials that readily allow electrons to flow are called *conductors*, and those that do not are called *nonconductors* (Fig. 1-11).

Some common conductors are copper, iron, gold, and silver.

Some common nonconductors are rubber, glass, and a number of plastics.

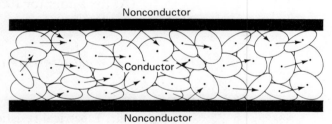

FIG. 1-11 Conductors versus nonconductors.

Air is also a good nonconductor. That is why it takes as much as 30,000 V of electrical pressure in an automotive ignition system to push an arc across the spark plug's air gap.

Conductors are used to delivery electricity; nonconductors to block it. The inside of a typical spark plug cable is made of a graphite composition, which is a conductor. The outside part of the cable, called the *insulation*, is made of rubber, a nonconductor used to prevent electricity from escaping.

1. *Why are some materials conductors and others nonconductors?*

2. *What are some common conductors?*

3. *What are some common nonconductors?*

4. *In a a spark plug cable, what is the conductor and what is the nonconductor?*

OHM'S LAW

When thinking about volts, amps, and ohms, it is important to regard them as related quantities. In a given circuit, whenever one of these quantities changes, the others must also change.

For instance, suppose that one of the wires became frayed in the headlight circuit of an automobile. This means that the ohms of resistance have increased. What happens to the amperage at the headlamp bulb, assuming that voltage has remained the same?

Because the ohms of resistance have increased, the amperage has been reduced. Because of the resistance in the circuit, fewer electrons can be pushed through and the light will become dim.

In the example above, the voltage was assumed to remain the same. What would happen to the amperage in a circuit if the ohms didn't change but the voltage went up?

If the voltage or electrical pressure increases and the ohms of resistance remain the same, the quantity of electrical flow or the amperage must also increase.

Volts, amps, and ohms can be imagined as slices of a pie (Fig. 1-12). Whenever you change the size of one slice, the other slices must also change.

This is the Ohm's Law pie. It is used to find one quantity when the other two are known.

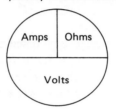

To find volts, multiply across the amps and ohm's:

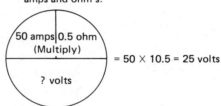

$$= 50 \times 10.5 = 25 \text{ volts}$$

To find ohms, divide the amps down into the volts:

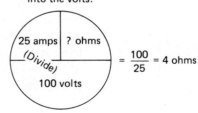

$$= \frac{100}{25} = 4 \text{ ohms}$$

To find amps, divide the ohms down into the volts:

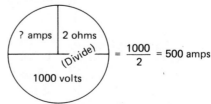

$$= \frac{1000}{2} = 500 \text{ amps}$$

FIG. 1-12   Ohm's law pie.

The relationship between volts, amps, and ohms is called *Ohm's Law*. It is described by one simple formula:

$$\text{volts} = \text{amps} \times \text{ohms}$$

and two variations on that formula:

$$\text{amps} = \frac{\text{volts}}{\text{ohms}}$$

$$\text{ohms} = \frac{\text{volts}}{\text{amps}}$$

In physics, the formula is usually represented as

$$E = I \times R$$

where E = volts or electromotive force
          I = amperage
          R = resistance

To see how the formula operates, imagine that in a given circuit, you have found that there are 12 V of electrical pressure and 0.24 ohm of resistance. To find the amps delivered by this circuit you would work the second formula, dividing 12 V by 0.24 ohm:

$$\text{amps} = \frac{12}{0.24}$$

This tells you that the circuit can deliver 50 A of current.

Now suppose that the wire becomes frayed and the ohms of resistance increase to 1.00. To see how many amps would be delivered, you would divide 12 by 1 (e.g., work the second formula again). This lets you know that the increase in resistance has dropped the amps down to 12.

Now suppose that you wanted to know how much voltage it would take to overcome the 1 ohm of resistance and deliver 50 A again. Although you could use any of the formulas to solve this problem, it is easiest to use the first formula, since you already know ohms and amps (1 and 50). Multiplying 1 times 50 tells you that 50 V would be needed to deliver 50 A past 1 ohm of resistance.

1. *What must happen in a given electrical circuit, if either volts, amps, or ohms change?*

2. *In a given circuit, if the ohms increase and the volts remain the same, what happens to the amps?*

3. *What do you call the relationship between volts, amps, and ohms?*

4. *What is the formula that describes this relationship?*

chapter
2

Simple Circuits

INTRODUCTION Consider the word *circuit*. It has a variety of meanings, all of which are related. For instance, a circuit judge is a legal expert who travels from court to court administering the law. A tennis circuit is a series of games played in different locales. And a circuit-riding parson is a minister who goes from place to place to do his preaching. In all these examples, the common factor is movement—something or someone going from one place to another.

The same idea applies to an electrical circuit. It is a continuous path along which electrons move, going from the source of electromotive force (battery and/or alternator) through the conductors, through the components in the circuit, and finally back to the source. There are two basic kinds of circuits, series and parallel; and several basic circuit conditions: open, closed, shorted, and so on. This chapter examines simple circuits and explains these terms.

ELECTRICAL SYMBOLS Electrical circuits are usually represented pictorially in diagrams. The various electrical components in the circuit and the connecting wiring are drawn on the diagram. Usually, realistic, detailed pictures of the

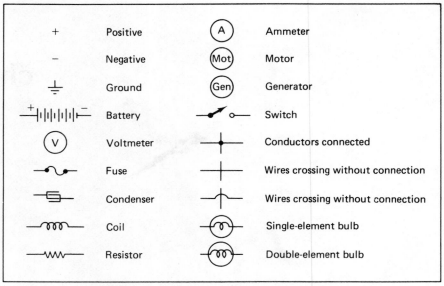

FIG. 2-1 Some common electrical symbols.

components are not used. It would take too much time, even for a skilled artist, to literally illustrate a circuit.

To save time and simplify matters, certain electrical symbols are used. Figure 2-1 describes some of the electrical symbols.

1. *Find the electrical symbol for an electric motor.*
2. *What is the symbol for a coil?*

A SIMPLE CIRCUIT Figure 2-2 is a picture (or schematic drawing as it is usually called) of a very simple circuit. This circuit includes a battery, a switch, electrical wires, and a single-element light bulb.

The different parts of the circuit are represented by symbols. The battery symbol is made up of long and short vertical lines. A pair of these long and short lines represents a single cell in the storage battery. The battery shown in Fig. 2-2 has six pairs of these lines, so it is a 12-V battery. (Also notice that the long line represents the positive terminal and the short line the negative terminal.)

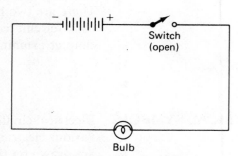

FIG. 2-2 Simple circuit.

1. Name the components of the simple circuit pictured in Fig. 2-2.

2. If a battery is represented by three pairs of long and short lines, how many volts will the battery produce?

OPEN AND CLOSED CIRCUITS

The circuit represented in Fig. 2-2 is called an *open* or *broken* circuit. That is because the switch symbol is in the open position. There is nothing but air between the two parts of the switch.

However, if the switch were closed, the circuit would be *complete* or *closed*. Electrons would then have an uninterrupted flow path from the negative terminal of the battery through the conducting wires, through the bulb's incandescent filament, past the closed switch, and back to the battery's positive terminal. The electron flow through the bulb's wire filament would knock loose photons (bundles of illumination, roughly speaking) and produce light.

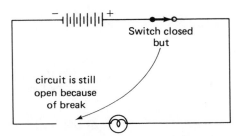

FIG. 2-3 Open, or broken, circuit.

In this example, the circuit is opened and closed by a switch. As illustrated in Fig. 2-3, the continuity of the circuit is also broken if the bulb's filament is burned out, if one of the battery leads is detached, or if there is a break in a wire. In brief, any gap in an electrical circuit will cause an interruption in the electrical flow.

1. When the contacts of a switch are separated by an air gap, is the electrical circuit connected to the switch opened or closed?

2. What are some other ways in which the continuity of a circuit can be broken?

GROUND RETURN CIRCUITS

In the circuits pictured in Figs. 2-2 and 2-3, metal wires conduct electricity from the battery. In an automobile, a portion of most circuits is replaced by the car's frame, body, and engine. This is possible because the frame, body, and engine, although made from different kinds of metals, are all electrical conductors, like the metal conducting wire.

The part of the circuit formed by the metal components of the car is often called the *ground return circuit*, or simply *ground*. In all American cars and in most imported vehicles, the negative terminal

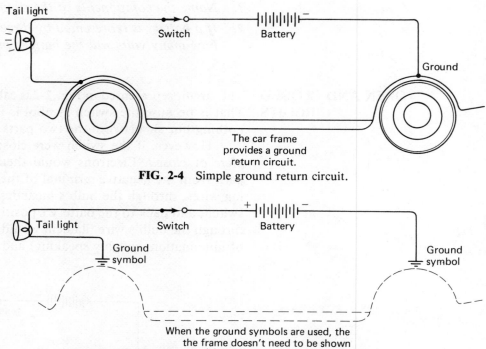

FIG. 2-4   Simple ground return circuit.

FIG. 2-5   Circuit shown in Fig. 2-4, with the car frame replaced by the electrical symbol for ground.

of the battery is connected to the frame or engine block. Hence, these cars are said to have a negative ground electrical system.

Figure 2-4 shows a simple ground return circuit. Note that it has the same electrical components as in Figs. 2-2 and 2-3. The only difference is that the car frame has replaced some of the wire conductors in the circuit.

Figure 2-5 shows the same circuit except that the car frame has been replaced by the electrical symbol for ground. Whenever you see these triangular-shaped notations, you know that the component pictured is connected to ground.

1. What part of the car replaces one side of most electrical circuits in an automobile?

2. Are most American cars positively or negatively grounded?

SHORTED AND GROUNDED CIRCUITS

Electrical cables and wires snake all around a car's frame, body, and engine. The only thing that keeps these circuits separate is the rubber or plastic insulation around the wires. If this nonconductive insulation is damaged or frayed and one of the wires contacts another wire or the wrong part of the car, a *shorted* or *grounded* circuit will result.

A shorted (or grounded) circuit is just what the name implies, a circuit whose length has been reduced. It is not like a broken circuit because current still flows; it just doesn't have as far to go.

The terms "shorted" and "grounded" mean much the same

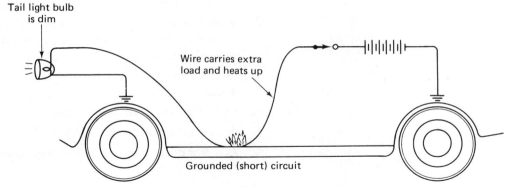

FIG. 2-6 Simple grounded condition.

thing. When two wires accidentally come in contact, it is called a *short*. When a wire touches the car body, frame, or engine in the wrong place, it is called a *ground*. Technically speaking, both are short circuits; the term "ground" is used because it is more descriptive of that particular condition.

Figure 2-6 illustrates a very simple grounded condition. The wire going from the battery to the tail light bulb has become frayed, allowing the metal conductor to touch the car's frame about halfway between the battery and the tail light. As a result, the current has two possible flow paths. Besides going to the tail light, it can also return to the battery by way of the car's frame.

Most of the current will take the shorter circuit back to the battery. The car's frame is much larger than the filament in the tail light bulb and it is much easier for the current to travel through the frame than through the bulb. It has fewer ohms of resistance.

Several things happen as a result of this ground or short circuit:

1. The tail light bulb will not burn at all or only very dimly, depending on how much current trickles past the "ground."

2. Normally, the tail light bulb's filament would only allow relatively small amounts of current to flow through the wire. However, when the conductor comes in contact with the car's frame, it is like opening up a flood gate. The grounded path offers very little resistance to current flow and the battery attempts to pump more and more electrons through the wires leading up to the ground point. If the ground condition is bad enough, the battery can become drained.

3. The wire leading up to the ground point is only designed to handle the current flow allowed by the tail light filament. The extra electrons being pushed toward the ground point cannot move easily through the wire. This causes a great deal of jostling among the electrons in the wire, with a resulting increase in molecular activity. As you learned earlier, molecular activity is directly related to heat, so as more and more electrons are bounced about inside the wire, the hotter the wire becomes. If the situation continues, the wire will become hot enough to melt its insulating wrapping and perhaps start a fire.

1. *Does current continue flowing in a short or ground circuit?*

2. *When a ground circuit occurs, does the current "prefer" to follow along its original path or go to the battery by way of the new, "shorter" circuit?*

3. *In the example illustrated in Fig. 2-6, which has the greatest resistance, the original path through the tail light filaments or the new path through the frame?*

4. *What are some of the effects of a short or ground circuit?*

5. *Is a fire a danger in a short or grounded circuit, and if so, why?*

CIRCUIT PROTECTORS   Fortunately, there are various devices to protect a circuit against a short or ground condition. One is the *fuse* (Fig. 2-7). Fuses are simply strips of metal designed to melt under the heat of excessive current loads (Fig. 2-8). (All current flow involves electron movement and some degree of heating.) The normal current flowing through the fuse will not melt the metal strip. But if the circuit of which the fuse is a part has a short or ground condition allowing excess current to flow, the fuse will melt. This creates an air gap or broken circuit through which no current can flow. Thus, the circuit will be protected against further heat damage. In effect, the fuse is a designed-in weak spot in the circuit.

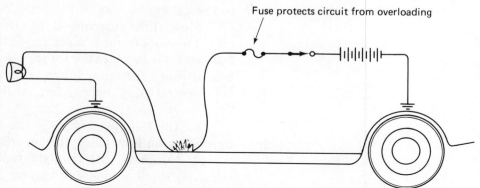

FIG. 2-7   The fuse is one device that protects a circuit against a short or grounded condition.

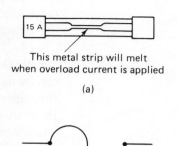

FIG. 2-8   (a) Actual fuse. (b) Fuse symbol.

There are various fuses with various capacities for different circuits. Some fuses are encased in glass tubes. Others are set in ceramic insulators. Most have the capacity stamped somewhere on the body.

Another kind of circuit protector is the breaker switch. It uses a bimetallic spring. The bimetallic spring is made from two pieces of dissimilar metal sandwiched together. When current passes through the sandwich, the two kinds of metal heat up and expand, but at different rates. This causes the spring to bend. If the spring is incorporated into a switch, excessive current flow will cause the spring to bend sufficiently to open the switch and break the circuit. Then when the spring cools, the spring bends back to close the circuit. Such a breaker does not completely shut down a circuit. By switching on and off, it warns the driver that something is wrong.

1.   How are fuses different from circuit breakers?

SERIES CIRCUITS   There are two basic kinds of electrical circuits, series and parallel. The primary difference is that *series circuits* provide only one path for current flow, whereas *parallel circuits* offer a variety of paths.

Figure 2-9, is an example of a simple series circuit. It has a battery, a switch, and three single-element light bulbs. There is only one path for current to flow in this circuit. It must go from the battery through each of the bulbs. If one of the bulbs should fail, it will break the entire circuit and no current can pass. For this reason, series circuits are not used extensively in automobiles.

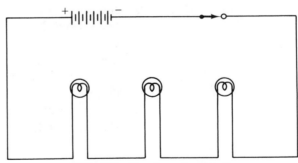

FIG. 2-9   Simple series circuit.

1.   What is the primary difference between series and parallel circuits?

2.   What happens to the entire circuit if a single element in a series circuit fails?

3.   Some automotive components use series circuits. Examine the electrical flow path in a multicell battery and decide what kind of circuit it uses.

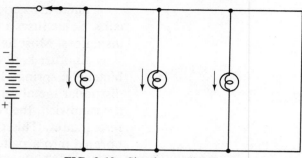

FIG. 2-10 Simple parallel circuit.

PARALLEL CIRCUITS

Parallel circuits are just the opposite of series circuits. Instead of one possible flow path, the current can follow several routes. Figure 2-10 illustrates a simple parallel circuit. It has the same basic elements as the series circuit shown in Fig. 2-9, except that more flow paths are provided. For this reason, one element in the circuit can fail and current will still flow along the other paths to the other elements. For instance, if one of the bulbs in Fig. 2-10 burns out, the current can still go to the other bulbs. In order for the entire circuit to be broken, either the switch must be opened or the elements in all the bulbs must fail.

1. The headlights in a car are connected in parallel. So if one light fails, will the others go out?

FIGURING RESISTANCE IN CIRCUITS

Each of the elements in a circuit, the devices that use electricity and the wires that carry it, offer a certain amount of resistance to electrical flow. Knowing the resistance of the items (such as the resistance of various size copper wires as noted in Fig. 2-11), it is possible to determine the resistance of the entire circuit. However, the effects of each element on the total resistance is different for series and parallel circuits.

A series circuit is somewhat like a single-lane road (Fig. 2-12). Each driver (or electron) on the road must overcome the same obsta-

Wire size (AWG)	Resistance (ohms/1000 ft)
6	0.465
8	0.739
10	1.18
12	1.87
14	2.97
16	4.73
18	7.51
20	11.9
22	19.0
24	30.2

FIG. 2-11 Resistance of copper wire.

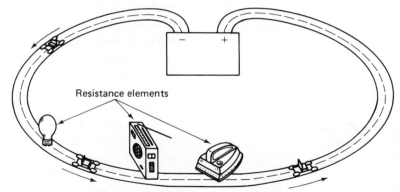

FIG. 2-12 A series circuit is like a single road. All the resistance must be overcome by every electron. The total resistance is equal to all the resistances added together.

cles or resistances—the same curves, hills, bumps, and so on. By the end of the road, every driver has had to overcome the total of all the resistances of the road.

A parallel circuit, however, is like a branching network of roads (Fig. 2-13). Some drivers follow paths of high resistance and some

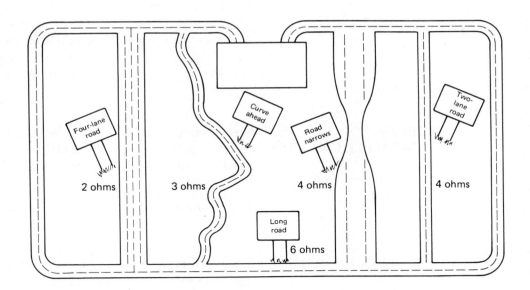

$$\frac{1}{R_T} = \frac{1}{R_1} + \frac{1}{R_2} + \frac{1}{R_3} + \text{etc.}$$

$$\frac{1}{R_T} = \frac{1}{2} + \frac{1}{3} + \frac{1}{4} + \frac{1}{4} + \frac{1}{6}$$

$$\frac{1}{R_T} = \frac{6 + 4 + 3 + 3 + 2}{12}$$

$$\frac{1}{R_T} \times \frac{18}{12}$$

$$R_T = \frac{12}{18} = 0.66 \text{ ohm (which is much less than the resistance in any single branch of the circuit)}$$

FIG. 2-13 A parallel circuit resembles a branching network of roads.

paths of low resistance. There are several possible ways to go from the start to the finish of the network, and the overall resistance is never greater than the resistance of the most difficult branch, because there is always an easier road available. The resistance in each path affects that path only. In fact, the more roads that are added to a network, the less the overall resistance. That is true because a circuit that has more paths can handle more electrons.

Figure 2-12 shows the mathematical way to add resistances in a series circuit. As you can see, the greater the number of resistance elements, the greater the overall resistance of the circuit.

Figure 2-13 pictures the proper method for figuring the resistance in a parallel circuit. If you follow the arithmetic, you will note that the overall resistance must be reduced when more branches are added to the circuit.

1. *On a single-lane road, do you have an opportunity to avoid any resistance elements along the road? How about a branching network of roads?*

2. *What happens to the overall resistance in a series circuit as you add resistance elements?*

3. *(fill in the blank) Suppose that you are designing a circuit that contains one high-resistance element and a number of low-resistance elements. You don't want the high-resistance component to block the current to the other elements, so you use a _____ circuit and put the high-resistance element in a branch by itself.*

COMBINATION SERIES/ PARALLEL CIRCUITS

Many actual circuits combine series and parallel paths. Figure 2-14 pictures such a circuit. The total resistance of a circuit like this is the parallel resistance plus the series resistance.

1. *Try to determine the total resistance of the circuit in Fig. 2-14.*

VOLTAGE DROP

Each resistance element in a circuit requires a certain amount of voltage to push a given amount of current past the resistance. Electrical wires and even the frame ground circuit offer some resistance to current flow and thereby use up some voltage.

The amount of voltage required to overcome the resistance in different parts of the circuit can be measured by a voltmeter. As pictured in Fig. 2-15, the two voltmeter leads are attached on either side of (or "across") each of the resistance elements. The amount of volts used by each element is read on the voltmeter dial. As you would expect from Ohm's Law, the high-resistance elements require more voltage to push a given amount of current than do the low-resistance elements.

The amount of voltage measured across each of the resistance elements is called the *voltage drop*. The voltage drop for element A in

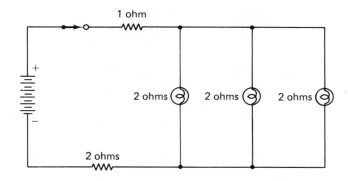

$$R_{series} = 1 + 2$$

$$\frac{1}{R_{parallel}} = \frac{1}{2} + \frac{1}{2} + \frac{1}{2}$$

$$R_{total} = R_{series} + R_{parallel}$$

FIG. 2-14 Combination series/parallel circuit.

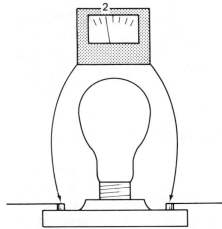

FIG. 2-15 Voltage drop is the actual voltage reading obtained when voltmeter probes are placed on both sides of a resistance element. The higher the resistance, the greater the voltage drop, since proportionally more current flows through the voltmeter.

Fig. 2-16 is 2 V, 5 V for element B, and 5 V for element C. All these voltage drops, when added together equal the total terminal voltage at the battery, in this case, 12 V.

Note: The term "voltage drop" is often confused. Remember: Voltage drop is the *actual* voltage measurement across a resistor element. When the resistance is high, the voltage measurement and hence the voltage drop will be high. Conversely, when the resistance to current flow is low, the voltage required (and the voltage drop) will be low.

1. What does it mean to "measure voltage across a resistance element"?

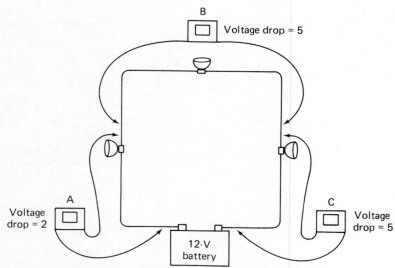

FIG. 2-16 The voltage drop of all the elements in a circuit equals the voltage potential of the source.

2. *What term is used to describe the amount of voltage measured across the resistance elements in a circuit?*

3. *When a component offers high resistance to current flow, will the voltage drop measured across that component be high or low?*

CIRCUIT TESTING   You might be wondering what practical use concepts such as voltage drop, circuit resistance, and Ohm's Law have in automechanics. As it so happens, testing and repairing automotive electrical components would be very difficult without an understanding of these and other terms. For instance, the resistance of automotive circuits and the elements in those circuits are usually specified by manufacturers in terms of voltage drop. So to perform and understand the significance of the voltage drop test, you not only need to know what voltage drop is, but you must also know how volts, amps, and ohms are related in Ohm's Law.

chapter

3

Batteries

INTRODUCTION

There are two main energy sources in an automobile (aside from the driver). One, the fuel, supplies the power needed to operate the engine and move the vehicle from place to place. The other source, the battery, provides the power needed to liberate the fuel's energy. The battery also supplies the power for the accessories, the starter motor, and so on.

All of the electrical components together make up the automotive electrical system. The battery is the heart of the system, plus a major part of each of the subsystems that make up the overall electrical system. This chapter examines the operation of the battery.

BASIC BATTERY OPERATION

The battery is a source of electrical energy because it can cause electron movement in any conductor attached to the battery's two terminals. The positive terminal pulls electrons from the conductor and the negative terminal pushes electrons back into the conductor, resulting in a continuous current flow. Therefore, the secret of the battery's power is its ability to move electrons.

Before going on, it will be helpful to discuss briefly this ability to push and pull electrons as it is illustrated by a very simplified type of battery.

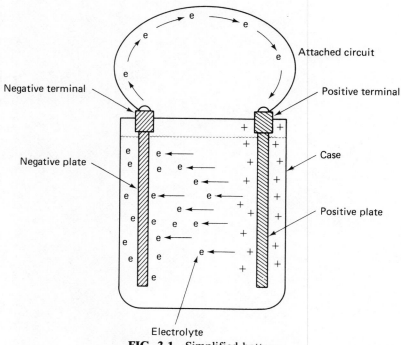

FIG. 3-1 Simplified battery.

The components of the simplified battery (Fig. 3-1) are (1) a pair of dissimilar metal plates, (2) positive and negative terminals attached to these plates, (3) a chemically active liquid called electrolyte into which the plates are immersed, and (4) a container for the plates and the electrolyte.

Electrons are moved because of the chemical reaction between the electrolyte and the two kinds of plates. Very roughly speaking, the electrolyte allows electrons to move away from one kind of plate and build up on another. As a result, one kind of plate and its attached terminal will have more than the normal number of electrons. The other plate and its terminal will have fewer electrons. In the plate with fewer electrons, the positive protons will predominate, giving that plate and its terminal a positive charge. The plate and terminal with more electrons will have a negative charge.

This is the operation of a simplified battery. These same basic features can be expanded in a number of ways to create a more complex battery. For instance, extra pairs of positive and negative plates can be added, in a kind of alternating "sandwich" (as long as the layers don't touch). These extra plates will not increase the voltage or "push" given to any single electron released by any particular plate. However, the capacity of the battery is increased by increasing the total number of electrons put into motion.

The simplified battery can also be combined with other batteries (Fig. 3-2). Its positive and negative terminals can be joined to the opposite terminals of a second battery, that battery's terminals to the opposite terminals of a third battery, and so on. Joining batteries this way (positive to negative to positive to negative to positive and so on) will add to the total electrical "push" or voltage. For instance, if six

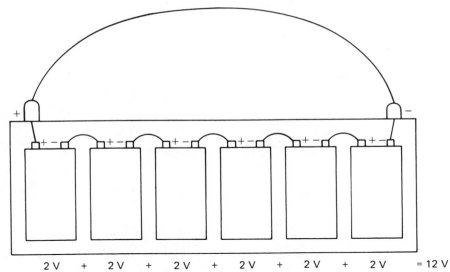

2 V   +   2 V   +   2 V   +   2 V   +   2 V   +   2 V   = 12 V

FIG. 3-2   Six individual "sub" batteries or cells are combined
in one larger battery to produce 12 V.

2-V batteries are joined together, the total pressure will be (6 × 2) =
12V.

When several small batteries are combined in one battery case,
the individual "sub" batteries are called "cells." So, in a way of
speaking, a six-cell, 12-V automotive battery is made up of six
smaller batteries.

1. *Why is a battery a source of electrical pressure?*
2. *What are the main components of the simplified battery described in this section?*
3. *What role (roughly speaking) does the electrolyte play in moving electrons from one plate to another?*
4. *Which has more electrons, a positive plate and its attached terminal or a negative plate?*
5. *Does increasing the size and number of the plates add to the voltage or the amperage?*
6. *Adding cells has what affect on voltage produced by a battery?*
7. *What is the voltage produced by a three-cell battery whose cells produce 2 V each?*

AUTOMOTIVE BATTERY CONSTRUCTION

Plates

Each cell in modern automotive batteries contains two groups of
plates, a positive plate group and a negative plate group (Fig. 3-3).
The negative plates are made of porous, electrically conductive,
sponge lead. The positive plates are also porous lead that has been

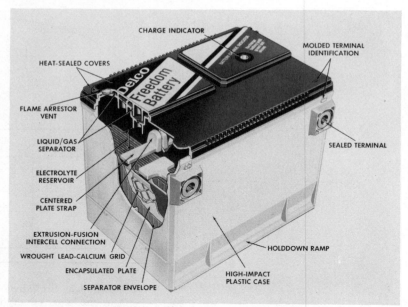

FIG. 3-3 In the cutaway section of this battery can be seen the honeycomb-like grid in which the plates are cast. (Courtesy Delco Division, General Motors.)

coated with lead peroxide paste. The plates are usually cast in a honeycomb-like grid (Fig. 3-3). The horizontal and vertical ribs of the grid are made from a lead antimony to give strength to the otherwise weak sponge construction.

Separators

If the alternating pairs of positive and negative plates touch, there will be no electron flow. To keep the plates apart, two kinds of separators are used. One kind is a nonconductive, porous sheet located between each of the positive and negative plates. The porous design allows electrolyte to flow between the plates. The nonconductive nature of the material (glass, plastic, wood, etc.) prevents the separators from entering into the chemical reactions. Most modern separators provide vertical passages or grooves so that particles broken loose from the spongy plate material can drop into the "catch area" at the bottom of the battery. This secondary, cleansing function of the separators greatly extends the life of the battery.

Connector strap separators

The other kind of separator is the plate connector strap. There is one connector strap for all the positive plates in a cell and another for all the negative plates. These cast lead, electrically conductive straps have several functions. They help separate the positive from the negative plates, as well as join the negative and positive plates into two separate groups. The straps also provide an electrical connection between the plates and the cell's terminals (the terminals, positive and negative, are where electrons enter and leave a cell). The strap connecting all the negative plates is joined to the cell's negative terminal and the strap connecting all the positive plates is joined to the cell's positive terminal. That way, an excess of electrons is built up not only on the negative plates, but also on the negative connector strap and the negative terminal. By the same token, there is a reduction of electrons on the positive plates, connector strap, and terminal.

Cell connectors

In order for current to flow between cells, the terminals of one cell must be joined to the opposite terminals in the next cell (positive to negative to positive and so on). In old-style batteries, the between-cell connectors were located in plain view on top of the battery. However, modern batteries locate the connectors out of sight inside the battery case. One style of cell connector goes over the partitions which divide the cells. In many newer batteries, the cell connector passes between the partitions. This reduces the distance the electrons have to travel and improves the battery's performance.

Battery posts

The connector straps at both ends of the battery are joined to the battery's external positive and negative posts. These external posts or terminals may be identified in a variety of ways. The positive post may be larger than the negative post, painted red, and/or marked (+) on top or (pos.) nearby. The negative terminal, in turn, may be smaller, painted green or black, and/or marked (−) on top or (neg.) nearby. The terminals may be on top of the battery or, in the newer "energizer batteries," may be on the side of the battery case.

Battery case

The battery case is the box or container which holds the plates, cells, and electrolyte. In the past, cases were constructed of wood coated with a tar substance to resist the corrosive action of the electrolyte. Modern battery boxes are made from a plastic, such as polypropylene. Not only are modern battery boxes able to resist the electrolyte better, they are also lighter and stronger, standing up longer under road shocks and vibration.

1. *What materials are used in the positive and negative plates in automobile batteries?*
2. *What is the function of the separator sheet?*
3. *What do the connector straps do besides separate the plates?*
4. *What are three kinds of cell connectors?*

5. *Name some ways that positive and negative battery posts may be identified.*

6. *What kinds of materials are used in modern battery cases?*

ELECTROLYTE   Electron flow is a three-way chemical reaction between the electrolyte and the two kinds of lead plates. In automotive batteries, the electrolyte is a solution of sulfuric acid and water, about 60% water and 40% acid. The sulfuric acid may be said (greatly oversimplifying a complex reaction) to pull electrons from the lead peroxide positive plates and allow electrons to build up on the negative sponge lead plates. This creates a "potential" for electron movement at the battery's two external terminals.

> ***Warning:*** Because the electrolyte is made up of a sulfuric acid solution, it is dangerous. Spilled electrolyte from a battery will destroy paint and metal. It will eat holes in your clothing, or your skin, and it will blind you if it gets in your eyes.

1. *What are the two ingredients in an electrolyte?*

DISCHARGING   The term "discharging" simply means that the battery is being used —that it is connected to a complete electrical circuit through which electrons can flow.

Discharging causes the active ingredients in the electrolyte to be used up. The sulfuric acid dissolved in water breaks down into two kinds of particles, both of which have an electrical charge. The positive particles are called hydrogen ions and the negative particles, sulfate ions. Positive and negative charges are also created on the surface of the lead plates.

Because these charged particles are unstable, they try to combine with one another to become electrically balanced. Positive hydrogen ions from the acid combine with negative oxygen ions from the lead peroxide plates to form water. And the negative sulfate ions from the electrolyte combine with the positive lead ions from both plates to form a chemically neutral coating on the plates called lead sulfate. The more the battery is discharged, the fewer active ingredients it contains, until finally the electrolyte becomes almost pure water.

Also, as the battery discharges, the tiny holes and crevices in the spongy lead plates become coated with the neutral lead sulfate. This renders the plates ineffective.

1. *What does "discharge" mean?*

2. *What happens to the electrolyte during discharging?*

3. *What happens to the plates?*

Charging

Fortunately, the effects of discharging in lead acid batteries are reversible. If a flow of electrons is forced through the battery in a direction opposite to the normal flow, the previous chemical reactions will reverse themselves. The sulfate ions from the plates and the hydrogen ions from the water will go back into the electrolyte. The battery will become active again.

When the engine is running, the battery is constantly being recharged by the alternator or generator (Fig. 3-4). The car's charging system takes some of the fuel's energy and converts it into electrical power.

Depending on the electrical load and the operating conditions, the charging system will supply current at a pressure of 12 to 14.5 V in a 12-V system. If the battery is used in normal service and if the charging system is adjusted properly, a battery should last 3 to 5 years. However, if the battery is used improperly, for instance if the lights are left on overnight or if the charging system is not functioning, the battery may discharge so much that it can't crank the car. In these cases, if the battery's plates are not too badly coated, the battery can be reactivated by an external battery charger (Fig. 3-5). It does the same job as the car's charging system and usually has two operating ranges: a fast charge and slow charge. The fast charge supplies a great deal of current at high voltage pressures so that the battery can be used sooner. The slow charge, which is generally safer

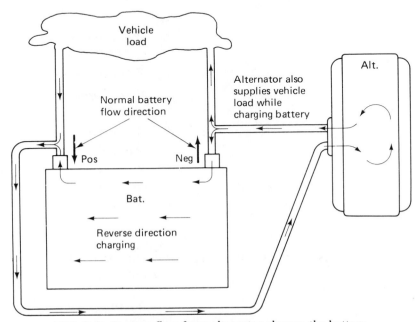

FIG. 3-4 Reverse flow from alternator charges the battery.

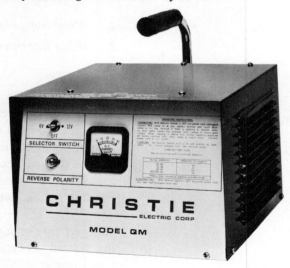

FIG. 3-5 External battery charger. (Courtesy Christie Corporation.)

and better, supplies a slow steady flow of current to gradually and thoroughly recharge the battery.

> ***Warning:*** When the battery is being charged, some of the water in the electrolyte is broken down into hydrogen and oxygen gases. This combination of gases is very explosive and great care must be taken to avoid sparks around any "gassing" battery. This is particularly true when a battery is being recharged at a fast rate by an external charger. Over the years a number of workers have blinded by exploding batteries.

1. *What happens to a battery when current is sent through in an opposite direction to normal flow?*
2. *What is the job of the car's charging system?*
3. *What happens to the battery if a car's headlights are left on overnight?*
4. *What are the two charging rates generally available with external chargers?*
5. *What kind of gases boil out of the electrolyte as a battery is being charged?*
6. *What happens if a spark is created in the presence of these gases?*

BATTERY FAILURE   Batteries do not last forever. Following are several ways that batteries can fail:

   1. Plate sulfation and electrolyte loss, as noted before, is a natural result of the discharging process. Up to a point, this process is reversible by recharging the battery—either using the car's own

charging system or, if the battery won't crank the car, an external charger. However, if the sulfation is too extensive, the battery must be junked.

2. Battery cells also simply wear out. Repeated charging and discharging will, after a time, knock the active ingredients from the lead plates. These ingredients fall to the sediment chamber at the bottom of the case to form an inactive lead sulfate sludge. When enough sludge is at the bottom of the case, the battery no longer has the ingredients to develop any power and must be discarded.

3. Batteries can also be damaged by various mechanical means. Road shocks and vibrations can loosen the plates and cause "tree"-shaped cracks in the separators and case. On occasion, a mechanic will pull an external post off trying to free a corroded battery cable.

4. Batteries are sometimes damaged by overcharging. This creates excess heat and causes gases to build up inside the cells. If the situation becomes bad enough, the plates, case, and separators may buckle.

5. An unused battery may damage itself simply because it is not being used. Unused batteries, unless they are emptied of electrolyte and stored dry, should be recharged from time to time. Otherwise, enough spontaneous chemical activity will take place to sulfate the plates and use up the electrolyte.

1. Describe the five kinds of battery failure noted in the preceding text.

BATTERY EFFICIENCY

Temperature

In the preceding chapter it was noted that atomic and molecular activity is dependent on temperature. When it is hot, electrons move faster, molecules bounce around quicker, and chemical reactions proceed at a faster rate. The opposite holds true when it is colder. Everything slows down until a theoretical point called absolute zero is reached. At that temperature (or no temperature) there is no atomic activity. Everything is motionless and dead.

These temperature/molecular-activity relationships hold true in a battery the same as they do anywhere in the universe. When it is cold, a battery's chemical reactions are sluggish and it develops less power. When the temperature goes up, the reactions speed up and the battery develops more power. So, batteries are more efficient at higher temperatures.

Discharge rate

Battery efficiency is also affected by the rate of discharge—in other words, by how much current the battery tries to move through a circuit connected to its terminals. When the resistance of the elements connected to the battery is low, it will try to push more electrons and its efficiency will be reduced. That is because the chemical reactions will all take place on the surface of the plates. The exchange of ions and electrons will not have time to penetrate into the interior of the spongy lead plates.

1. *What happens to electrical movement inside the battery as the temperature goes down?*
2. *Why would battery efficiency drop if you tried to crank a car with the radio, headlights, and cigarette lighter on?*

BATTERY RATINGS

Voltage output and variations

Each cell in a lead acid battery can produce about 2.13 V of electrical pressure (usually rounded off to 2 V). The cells can produce this voltage regardless of the size or number of the plates. However, the cell voltage rating is a maximum figure. In actual practice the voltage output may be less. Here are some of the factors that affect voltage output.

1. Temperature variations cause changes in voltage output. When the temperature is lower, the voltage is also lower.
2. The state of the electrolyte and the plates also affects voltage. When the electrolyte is weak and the plates sulfated, the voltage will drop.
3. Discharge rate also determines voltage output. When resistance to flow is reduced, the amperage will increase. And according to Ohm's Law, the voltage will have to drop in order to balance the equation. (Of course, all these changes in voltage and amperage follow the relationships laid down by Ohm's Law.)

Amperage output and rating

Batteries are usually rated by their ability to produce current at certain conditions. Following are some of these rating tests:

1. One popular way to rate batteries by the *twenty-hour test.* This measures the amount of current a battery can deliver for 20 hours, without the cell voltage dropping below 1.75. For instance, a battery might be able to deliver 5 A for 20 hours without the voltage dropping below 1.75. Usually, the results of this test are given in battery advertising in terms of "amp-hour" ratings. So the battery just described would be rated at 100 A-hours because it could deliver 5 A for 20 hours, or 100 A for 1 hour.
2. The *battery reserve test* measures the ability of a battery to supply current to the various accessories (lights, horn, radio, etc.)

when the charging system is not operating. The results of this test are given in terms of the time (hours, minutes, etc.) it takes for the voltage to drop below 10.5 when the battery is delivering current at the rate of 25 A.

3. The preceding two tests are performed on batteries at 80 degrees F. However, since the efficiency of the battery drops as the temperature goes down, it is also necessary to test the battery at cold temperatures. One *cold test* measures how long (hours, minutes, etc.) a battery at 0° F can deliver 300 A before the cell pressure drops to 1 V. Another cold test determines how many amperes a battery can delivery at 0° F and still maintain a pressure of 7.2 V. This later figure was chosen by the SAE (Society of Automotive Engineers) as the minimum voltage required to provide adequate cranking speed for large, modern, V-8 engines.

4. The *watt-hour test* is a measure of a battery's ability to perform work for a period of time. It is obtained by multiplying amp-hours times voltage. Some experts feel that rating a battery by its wattage potential is more accurate than the amp-hour method. They say that the amp-hour method does not distinguish well enough between the power capabilities of 6-V and 12-V batteries. For instance, a 6-V, 100 A-hour battery has more watts of power (6 × 100 = 600) than a 12-V, 45-A-hour battery (12 × 45 = 540).

1. *Name the four factors that affect voltage output.*
2. *What are some of the ways amperage output is rated?*

ELECTROLYTE SPECIFIC GRAVITY

Although battery service and testing will not be discussed until later, we should cover one point while the explanation of charging and discharging is still fresh in your mind. That point relates to testing the specific gravity of electrolyte.

As noted before, when the battery is discharged, the sulfuric acid in the electrolyte is used up. The active ingredients in the electrolyte combine with the lead plates, causing the elecrolyte to weigh less. The more the electrolyte weighs, the more acid it contains. The less it weighs, the less acid it will have.

The specific gravity test is simply a way to compare the weight of electrolyte with water. Water is said to have a specific gravity reading of 1.000. A battery filled with plain water would have virtually no electrical potential at its poles. So a battery whose electrolyte reads near 1 would have no power. All its acid would be used up and the electrolyte turned back to water.

However, a battery whose specific gravity is between 1.260 and 1.300 would be fully charged. In that range, the electrolyte contains all its active ingredients.

Specific gravity is usually tested by a device called a hydrometer. The example shown in Fig. 3-6 resembles a large medicine dropper. Each cell in a battery is checked by drawing a sample of electrolyte

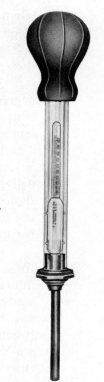

FIG. 3-6 Hydrometer.

into the hydrometer. A float is suspended in the electrolyte sample and the specific gravity determined by checking the level of the float against a scale. The higher the float rides in the sample of electrolyte, the denser the liquid and the greater the specific gravity. This procedure is covered in more detail later.

1. *What is the specific gravity of water?*
2. *What is the specific gravity range for the electrolyte in a fully charged battery?*
3. *What is the name of the device used to check specific gravity?*

chapter

4

Magnetism

INTRODUCTION Electricity is used by the automobile in several ways. Light bulbs use electric current to produce illumination. Spark plugs use an electric arc to ignite the air/fuel mixture. Most cars use the friction of electrons passing through certain kinds of wires to generate heat for particular devices. In all of these applications the desired effect takes place directly in the electron carrier—in other words, in the bulb's filament, at the spark plug's electrodes, and in the electric heater element.

The application of electricity described in this chapter is somewhat different. Instead of depending on the properties of electric flow in the carrier, the effects of electrical flow on space itself are used. This change in the nature of space is called *magnetism*.

DISCOVERY OF MAGNETISM Although electricity and magnetism are related, they are not the same thing. Magnetism was known and used long before electricity.

The actual discovery of magnetism is shrouded in legend. One tale relates the story of a Greek shepherd boy who wore sandals with iron tacks in the soles and carried a staff with an iron tip. While herding his sheep one day, he was suddenly pulled to the earth with great force. Digging into the ground to discover the nature of this mystery, he found a large stone with the power to attract iron.

If this story is true (which is unlikely), the stone was probably composed of the mineral magnetite. Magnetite is a black, ferrous (iron) compound named for a city in Asia Minor called Magnesia.

Whatever the circumstances of the original discovery, magnets were put to practical use about the twelfth century AD. It was discovered that a suspended magnet, if allowed to swing free, would always line up in a given direction. One end would always point north and the other end south. This property of magnets made possible the invention of the compass, which allowed sailors to venture across the oceans beyond sight of land.

1. What will a magnet always do if allowed to swing free?

PROPERTIES OF MAGNETS   Although no one knows exactly why magnets work the way they do, a great deal is known about what they do. For instance, it is known that all magnets have two distinct ends or poles. One of these ends is called the north pole (because if hung free it will always point north) and the other end is called the south pole. A magnet will always have these two poles, no matter how it is twisted, bent, or altered. Cut a single magnet in two and you will have two new magnets, each with north and south poles.

It has also been observed that these poles behave strangely around one another (Fig. 4-1). Place two alike poles together and they will push apart. Place two unalike poles nearby and they will try to come together. Magnets are able to exert a force over one another as well as iron objects without actually touching. It is as if some invisible ring of power surrounds the magnet.

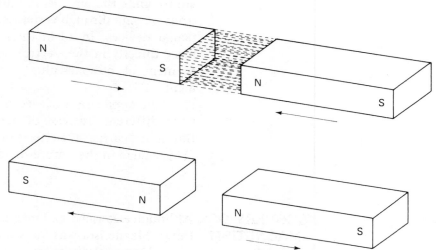

FIG. 4-1 Unlike poles of a magnet attract; like poles repel or oppose.

1. What would happen if the north poles of two magnets were brought together?

2. What would happen if a north and a south pole were placed nearby?

3. What seems to surround a magnet?

MAGNETIC FIELDS

The invisible ring of power surrounding a magnet is called the *magnetic field*. It does not have any "substance" in the conventional sense and appears to exist equally well in solids, air, and the vacuum of outer space. The best way to visualize this mysterious field is simply as a region of force or power extending from the magnet.

1. What do you call the invisible ring of power surrounding a magnet?

2. What is the best way to visualize this ring of power?

HOW MAGNETIC FIELDS ARE CREATED

Although no one knows exactly why magnetic fields exist, scientists have ideas about how they exist. One theory suggests that the movement of certain "inner-shell" electrons around atomic nuclei cause atoms to behave like tiny magnets. Each atom has its own magnetic field, with a north and a south pole.

In nonmagnetic materials (wood, plastic, glass, etc.), the atoms are jumbled up or in disarray [Fig. 4-2(a)]. Some poles point in one direction and some in another. So the total of all the magnetic fields or charges tend to cancel out. The substance has no distinct poles.

However, in magnetic or magnetized materials, many of the atoms tend to line up [Fig. 4-2(b)]. Their poles point in the same direction, and as a result the tiny force fields combine to give the material a definite orientation. No matter how it is cut, bent, or reshaped, each piece of the substance will have a north pole and a south pole.

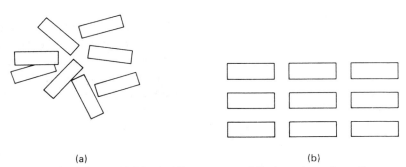

(a)   (b)

FIG. 4-2   (a) Bricks in disarray resemble the orientation of electrons in nonmagnetized material. (b) Here, as in magnetized material, the bricks all point in the same direction, thereby adding or lending their magnetic strength to each other.

1.   Why is each atom said to behave like a tiny magnet?

2.   Why don't nonmagnetic materials behave like magnets?

3.   What happens to the alignment of atoms in magnetized materials?

PERMANENT AND TEMPORARY MAGNETS

Most magnets can be divided into two basic categories, permanent and temporary. *Permanent magnets* can be fabricated from the mineral magnetite. However, most are made from steel or iron alloys which have been "stroked" or "rubbed" by magnetite or by some other magnetizing agent. This action aligns the atoms in the iron, allowing all the magnetic fields to add up and thus give the material its magnetic properties. Such man-made magnets, if cared for, will last a long time. However, when subjected to shocks or sudden blows, the atoms will become jumbled and the material will lose its magnetic properties.

Temporary magnets are made from soft-iron materials. They possess magnetic properties only as long as a magnetizing force is nearby. When the force is removed, the atoms will not remain lined up and the material will no longer be a magnet.

1.   What effect does rubbing magnetite across steel have on the steel?

2.   What happens to a temporary magnet if you remove the magnetizing force?

MAGNETIC LINES OF FORCE

Summarizing briefly: You have learned that magnets have north and south poles; that like poles repel and unlike poles attract; that both poles have the power to attract iron objects; and that magnets seem to be surrounded by an invisible ring of power called the magnetic field. What you haven't learned yet is that the magnetic field has a definite shape and its composed of "lines."

Shape

The shape of a magnetic field can be seen if you place a magnet under a piece of paper, then sprinkle iron filings on the paper. When the paper is tapped lightly, the filings will be pulled by magnetic attraction into the shape of the field (or more accurately, into the shape of that portion of the field sliced through by the paper). Figure 4-3 shows the shape of magnetic fields surrounding magnets arranged in several different ways.

Lines

As you may have noticed in the illustration, the iron filings arrange themselves roughly into lines. These lines are called the *magnetic lines of force or flux.* They are what make up the magnetic field. The

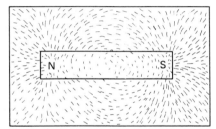

FIG. 4-3 A magnetic field can be visually observed by placing a bar magnet under a piece of paper and sprinkling the paper with iron filings. The paper should be tapped lightly while the filings are sprinkled on the surface.

lines extend from north to south poles. The magnetic field is strongest where the lines are closest together. Therefore, the field is strongest at the poles where the lines converge. The field is weakest midway between the poles where the lines separate.

Directional magnetic fields

Magnetic lines of force, like electrons in an electrical circuit, are said to move in particular directions and follow complete "circuits." In a bar magnet (Fig. 4-4), the lines of force move out from the north pole, travel across open space to the south pole, then move back through the magnet itself to come out again at the north pole. The lines of force follow a complete and continuous circuit. One part of the circuit is in the iron magnet and the other part is in the air, or whatever else that happens to be between the poles. A horseshoe magnet behaves in the same way. Lines of force extend from the north pole to the south pole, and then circles through the magnet to come out again at the north pole.

It is important to remember, though, that these force lines, patterns, movements, and fields can not be proven to exist in any real physical sense. They are simply descriptions of effects. Like so much

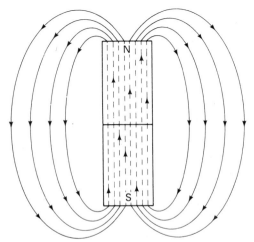

FIG. 4-4 Magnetic fields: bar magnets.

else in electricity, they are mental tools that help us visualize no-things in terms of some-things.

1.   *How can you determine the shape of a magnetic field?*
2.   *Where are the lines of force closest together?*
3.   *Where is a magnet's field the strongest: at the poles or between the poles?*
4.   *In which direction do magnetic lines of force move, from the north pole to the south or from the south pole to the north?*

MAGNETIC PERMEABILITY Even though magnetic lines of force can exist anywhere, they seem to prefer to pass through certain kinds of materials. Therefore, the shape of a magnetic field can change, depending on the kind of material that is nearby (Fig. 4-5).

The ability of a material to concentrate or pass lines of flux is called its *magnetic permeability.* Comparing the magnetic permeability of air, iron, and steel in the presence of equal magnetizing forces, air will pass 1 line of force; wrought iron, 1500 lines; and steel, 1000 lines. What this means in practical terms is that the power of a magnet can be concentrated and made more useful. In other words, although the overall power of a magnetic field might remain the same, its power in a particular region can be increased by using a high-magnetic-permeability material.

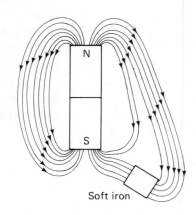

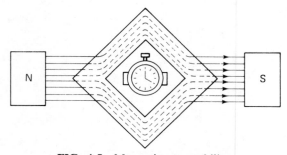

FIG. 4-5   Magnetic permeability.

Note: It should not be supposed that materials of low magnetic permeability can provide a magnetic shield. Remember: those imaginary lines of magnetic force can pass through anything and still have a real, nonimaginary effect on the other side. The only way to shield an object is to *divert* the lines of magnetic force away from the object by surrounding it with material of high magnetic permeability. Then the lines of force will "prefer" the shield to the shielded object. In this way, magnetic lines of force can be made to follow predetermined paths.

1. *How can the shape of a magnetic field be changed?*
2. *How can the power of a magnetic field be increased in a particular region around the magnet?*

ELECTROMAGNETISM There are two basic ways in which magnetic lines of force are created. One way is by a permanent magnet of some kind, whether naturally occurring or man-made.

The other way to create magnetic lines of force is by electricity. If you are wondering about temporary magnets, they don't actually create lines of force, but instead respond to some magnetizing agent, such as electricity.

As long ago as 1819, Hans Christian Oersted of Denmark noted a relationship between electricity and magnetism. He observed that a compass needle, if held near a wire carrying current, will swing around until it is at right angles to the wire. The needle is affected by a magnetic force coming from the wire. A discovery similar to that made by Oersted was made soon after by the Frenchman Andre Marie Ampère. He noted that current flowing in the same direction through two nearby wires will cause the wires to attract one another. He also observed that if the current flow in one of the wires is reversed, the wires will repel one another (Fig. 4-7).

What these scientists ultimately discovered is that the movement of electrons in a conductor will create a magnetic field around the conductor. Later-day physicists have gone on to speculate that the movement of electrons seems to line up (or polarize) the atoms so that many of their magnetic fields point in the same direction.

The shape of the electromagnetic field around a wire can be visualized, as before, by using iron filings. This time, a wire carrying current is passed through a piece of paper and the paper sprinkled with iron filings as shown in Fig. 4-8. When the paper is tapped, the filings will arrange themselves in concentric rings of force. The circular force lines are closer together near the wire, so that is where the magnetic field is strongest.

1. *What are the two basic ways in which magnetic lines of force are created?*

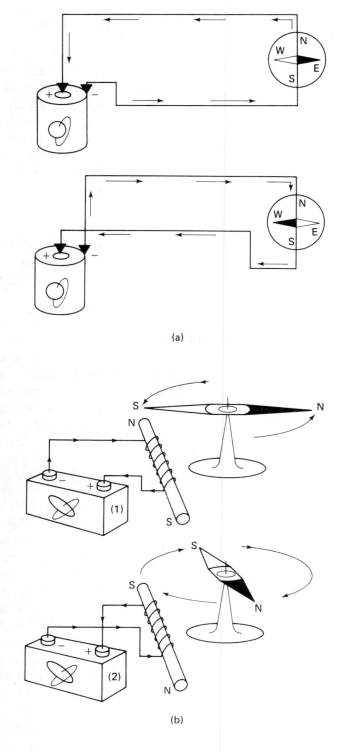

(a)

(b)

FIG. 4-6 (a) By the use of a length of wire, a dry cell battery, and a compass, it is easy to see the effect of reversing the polarity or direction of current flow through the wire or conductor. Small magnetic lines of force circle the current-carrying conductor, at right angles to the conductor. By reversing the direction of the current flow, swaping the leads on the cell, the lines of force are reversed and circle the wire in the opposite direction. Since all forces are in the form of concentric circles, either right or left, depending on which way the current is allowed to flow in, the compasses in each sketch will show the direction. The compass would ordinarily point due north or magnetic north. The presence of a local field would cause the compass to react to the concentric circles. Magnetic attraction diminishes with distance; therefore, the small field around the wires will easily affect the compass heading. (b) The poles of an electromagnet may be reversed in two ways should you wish to do so. The first way is to change the direction of current flow simply be exchanging the leads on the battery. Notice in the left-hand sketch that the north pole is at the top and is attracting the south pole of the compass. However, in the right-hand sketch the wires have been switched to the cell; now the current flows in the opposite direction and we find that the south pole is at the top of the sketch and is repelling the south tip of the compass, actually pushing it away. In the second way, the direction the wire is wound around the core will determine the north and south poles of the magnet. Assuming that the cell connections are not changed, the poles may be determined in advance by the direction in which the coil is wound.

2. *What happens to a compass needle when it is placed near a wire carrying current?*

3. *What happens to two nearby wires when both carry current going in the same direction? In opposite directions?*

4. *What is the pattern of the magnetic lines of force surrounding a wire?*

5. *Where is the magnetic field the strongest?*

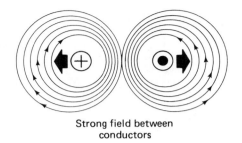

Strong field between
conductors

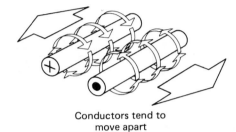

Conductors tend to
move apart

FIG. 4-7 If the current flows in opposite directions through nearby wires, the wires repel each other. If current flows in the same directions, the wires come together.

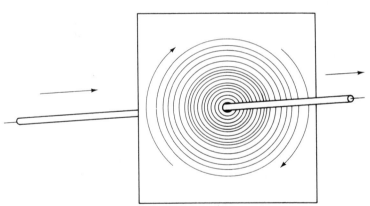

FIG. 4-8 A wire carrying current, passed through a piece of paper sprinkled with iron filings, shows the shape of the electromagnetic field around that wire..

DIRECTION OF MAGNETIC LINES OF FORCE THE LEFT-HAND RULE

Early investigators were quick to discover that the magnetic lines of force circling a wire seem to act in particular directions (like the lines of force around permanent magnets). For instance, in the compass experiment, the north end of the needle will point in a clockwise or counterclockwise direction, depending on the direction of the current flows through the wire. This indicates that the lines of force circle in one direction when the current flows one way and in the other direction when the current flow is reversed.

The direction taken by the lines of force around a wire is determined by a technique called the *left-hand rule* (Fig. 4-9). The rule states that if you grip a wire with your left hand, with your thumb pointing in the direction of current flow (from − to +), your

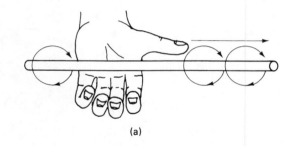

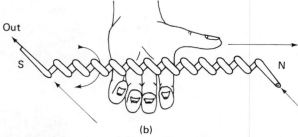

FIG. 4-9 (a) The left-hand rule for conductors states that if the left hand grips the conductor, with the thumb pointing in the direction of current flow, the fingers will point in the direction of rotation of the magnetic lines circling the conductor. (b) We can determine the north pole of a coil by use of the left-hand rule.

fingers will curl around the wire in the direction of the magnetic lines of force.

1. *What happens to a compass needle held near a wire if the current flow in the wire is reversed?*
2. *How do you determine the direction of magnetic lines of force around a wire?*

ELECTROMAGNETIC ATTRACTION AND REPULSION

Electromagnetism would just be an interesting scientific novelty if it were not put to some practical use. Ampère provided the key to many applications when he discovered that adjacent wires are attracted when their current flows in the same direction and repulsed when the current flow is reversed. This gives lines of force the ability to do mechanical work. Following is an analysis of what happens (Fig. 4-10):

1. When current flows in the same direction in adjacent wires, the lines of force circle in the same direction.
2. Lines of force try to follow the shortest path around a source of magnetic flux.
3. In order to follow the shortest path, the lines of force combine, going around all the wires as a group instead of around the individual wires. This merging action between the lines of force tends to pull the wires together. (It is similar to

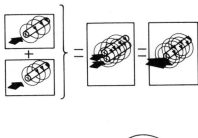

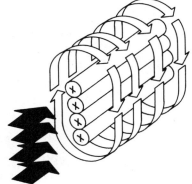

FIG. 4-10   Magnetic fields add together.

what happens when the north and south poles of two bar magnets are close together. The lines of force coming out of the north pole of one magnet join the lines of force going into the south pole of the other magnet. As the force lines merge, they pull the two magnets together, in effect creating a single magnet of extra strength.)

However, when current flows in the opposite direction in adjacent wires, the situation is reversed. The lines of force circle in opposite directions, and since force lines moving in opposite directions can neither cross nor join, they tend to push apart and separate. In so doing, the current-carrying wires are also pushed apart.

1.   *When current flows in the same direction in adjacent wires, do the force fields circle in the same or opposite directions?*

2.   *In question 1, why do the force lines combine to go around all wires as a group?*

3.   *Why can't the force lines join up when the current flow in adjacent wires is opposite?*

ELECTROMAGNETS   Electromagnetism can be used to create magnets. To see how, visualize a wire coiled into a series of loops (Fig. 4-11). Current flowing through the wire will move in the same direction in adjacent loops. So, according to the previous section, the lines of force will join into one concentrated field circling all the loops. These moving lines of force will give the coil a magnetic orientation with north and

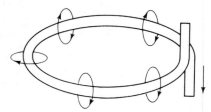

Fig. 4-11 In a coil lines of force circle through the center of the coil.

south poles and the ability to attract iron objects. The electromagnet behaves the same and can be used in the same way as a permanent magnet. The principal differences are that it can be turned on and off by interrupting the power flow, and that its polarity can be changed by reversing the direction of the current.

1. What happens to the lines of force circling an individual strand of wire if the wire is coiled into a series of loops?

2. How is an electromagnet different from a permanent magnet?

DETERMINING THE STRENGTH OF ELECTROMAGNETS

The strength of an electromagnetic coil is based on the number of turns or loops in the coil and on the amount of amperage delivered. For this reason, electromagnetic coils are usually described as having so many *ampere turns* of power.

The strength of a coil is also affected by the nature of the core material inside the coil. Loops of wire wrapped around an iron core will produce a local field 300% stronger than will loops wrapped around a paper tube with nothing but air inside (Fig. 4-12). One reason is that more lines of force travel through the iron core than through the air. The field is thereby concentrated and strengthened.

1. What does the term "ampere turns" of power mean?

2. How much more powerful is a coil with an iron core than one with an air core?

INDUCED CURRENT FLOW

The relationship between magnetism and electricity is strange and complex. As noted earlier, electrons moving along a wire will create a magnetic field. However, it is also possible to do just the opposite, to create electrical movement in a wire by using a magnetic field.

To see how this works, imagine a horseshoe magnetic being passed over a wire (Fig. 4-13). The magnet's lines of force, as they travel between the poles, cut across and wrap around the wire. The lines penetrate into the very atomic structure of the wire. As a result, the electrical balance of the atoms is upset and electrons are put into motion along the wire (as long as the wire is attached to a complete circuit).

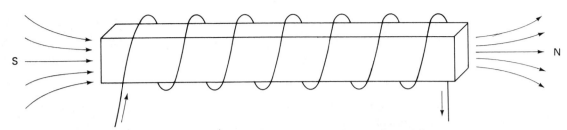

FIG. 4-12 The iron core concentrations these line of force, producing a stronger field.

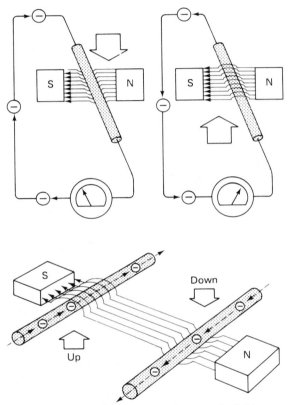

FIG. 4-13 Conductors and magnetic fields.

The direction of the electron flow is determined by the motion of the lines of force across the wire. If (relatively speaking) the lines of force cut *down* across the conductor, the current will flow in one particular direction. But, if the lines of force move *up* across the conductor, the current will flow in the opposite direction.

Note: It should be remembered that it does not make any difference if the conductor moves across the lines of force or if the lines of force move across the conductor. All that matters is that there is relative motion between the two. When there is, current flow is induced in the conductor.

1. *What happens when lines of force wrap or cut across a wire that is part of an electrical circuit?*

2. *What determines the direction of current flow?*

3. *Does it make any difference if the conductor moves across the lines of force or if the lines of force move across the conductor?*

BASIC OPERATION OF ELECTROMAGNETIC DEVICES

You are now ready to be introduced to the basic operation of several automotive components that use electromagnetism:

the electric generator (and alternator)
the electric motor
the solenoid coil
the ignition coil transformer

This brief introductory material will be followed by more detailed explanation in later chapters.

THE ELECTRIC GENERATOR (AND ALTERNATOR)

Basic principles

Current is produced whenever a conductor moves across magnetic lines of force (or vice versa). The direction of the current flow is determined by the path of the conductor across the lines of force, up or down, backward or forward, and so on.

All generators, whether in an automobile, a power generating station, or wherever, operate on these basic principles.

Figure 4-14 illustrates a very simple generator. It contains a magnet with lines of force moving from the north to the south pole. Rotating between the poles and cutting across the lines of force is a loop-shaped conductor. The ends of the loop are attached to slip rings which rub against carbon brushes. The brushes are attached to wires which run to the rest of the circuit.

When the conductor rotates in the magnetic field, the lines of force wrap around the two sides of the loop. At any given moment, one side of the loop is cutting down through the lines of force while the other side cuts up across the lines. The wrapping or cutting action causes electrons to move through the conductor, out one of the slip rings, through the entire circuit, and then back through the other slip ring.

Alternating current

Electron flow in the generator just described does not proceed in a constant direction. That is because the two sides of the conductor loop cut across the lines of force in an *alternating direction*. As the loop rotates, a given side will first cut *down* across the lines of force,

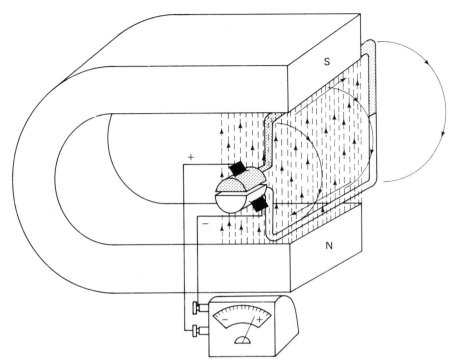

FIG. 4-14 As a conductor passes through a magnetic field, electrical voltage builds up. If this conductor is a part of a complete circuit, current flows. The direction of flow is determined by the direction of the conductor movement.

then cut back *up* through them, then back down, and so on. The effect is an *alternating current* direction or, as it is commonly called an *ac current*.

Household current in this country is usually of the ac variety, changing direction 60 times a second (making it easy to time the operation of electric clocks). However, ac current will not work in automobiles. That is because the battery moves electrons in one direction only, from the negative to the positive pole. The battery is a *direct-current* or *dc* device and requires direct current for recharging. so the ac output from the generator is changed to dc.

DC generators

Older-style automobiles use a mechanical commutator to change ac to dc. Figure 4-15 illustrates a simple commutator. It consists of two brushes and a single slip ring cut into two halves. Each half of the slip ring or commutator is connected to one side of the loop. While the loop rotates, each slip ring half rubs against first one brush, then the other. As a result, the current generated in each side of the loop first *pushes* through one brush, then *pulls* through the other brush. Just as the current from a given loop side is about to change directions, it is switched by the split commutator ring to the other side of the circuit. So throughout the overall circuit, current flow remains the same.

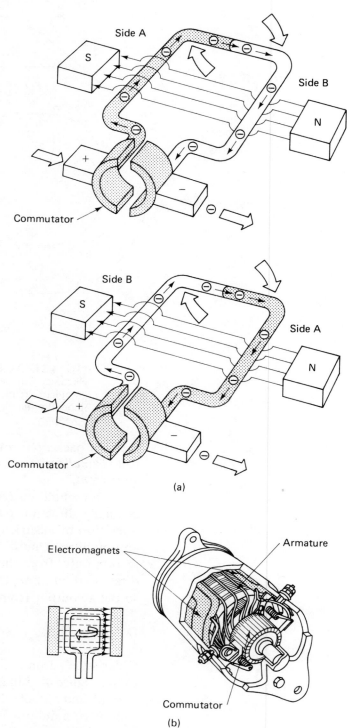

FIG. 4-15   (a) Commutator's action. (b) Generator.

Alternators

Most modern cars use an alternator to produce ac current. It is like a generator, except that the magnetic field is in the center of the assembly and rotates (Fig. 4-16). As it rotates, the lines of force cut

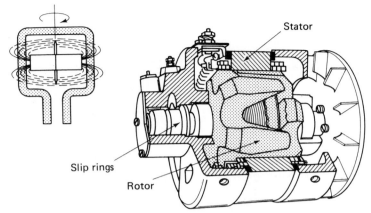

FIG. 4-16 Alternator.

across the stationary conductors loops that surround the interior magnetic field.

As you learned in the preceding, the effect is the same as long as there is relative movement between the conductor and the lines of force. So electrons are put into movement even though the conductor remains stationary. However, there is one consequence of allowing the conductor loops to remain stationary. A conventional split-ring commutator cannot be used to change the ac current to dc. Instead, the alternator uses diodes to rectify the ac to dc.

1. *What happens when the conductor loop in a generator moves across the lines of force?*

2. *What rubs against the slip rings?*

3. *What happens to current direction as a given side of the loop first cuts down across the lines of force, then moves up?*

4. *What is a mechanical commutator, and what does it do?*

5. *What rotates in an alternator, the magnetic field, or the conducting loops?*

6. *What does an alternator use to rectify ac to dc current?*

ELECTRIC MOTORS   An electric motor (like the starter motor or windshield motor) is just the opposite of a generator. Instead of *producing* current from the conductor windings (called the armature) current is sent *through* the armature as well as the electromagnetic field windings (called the *field*). This creates regions of magnetic attraction and repulsion between the lines of force surrounding the armature and field (Fig. 4-17). The resultant magnetic reaction causes the armature, and anything connected to it, to rotate.

To help understand this action, recall the behavior of two side-by-side wires carrying current. The wires will be attracted if the current flow is in the same direction or repelled if the flow in one wire is reversed. That is because the lines of force move in the same direction

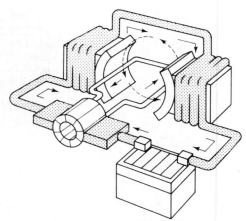

FIG. 4-17   Electric motor.

in one case and can join up. In the other case, they move in the opposite direction and must repel one another. The same kind of thing happens in an electric motor. The lines of force circling around the armature windings are alternately attracted and repelled by the lines of force coming from the field windings.

1.   *How is an electric motor different from a generator?*
2.   *What sort of reaction between the armature and the field causes the armature to rotate?*

THE SOLENOID COIL   Imagine you have wrapped a number of turns of wire around a paper tube, then connected the wire to a source of electromotive force (or EMF). As you learned previously, the lines of force circling adjacent loops will combine to form a single magnetic field extending all around the tube, both inside and outside (Fig. 4-18).

Now imagine that you have placed a steel nail near the end of the tube. If the electromagnet you made has sufficient ampere turns

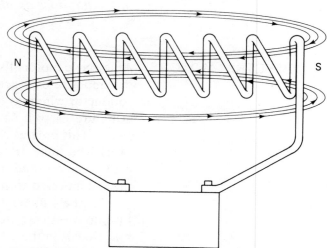

FIG. 4-18   Magnetic lines of force circle through a coil of wire, causing the coil to act like a permanent magnet.

of power, it will draw the nail inside the tube. It will act like a "hollow" permanent magnet capable of attracting iron and steel objects into its empty core. This kind of electromagnet is the basis of the solenoid coil, which is widely used as a switching and control device. You will see more of it later.

1. *Describe the operation of the simple solenoid coil described in the preceding text.*

IGNITION COIL TRANSFORMER

Here is another exercise: Imagine that you have two nearby coils of wire (Fig. 4-19). One coil, called the *primary* is attached to a source of EMF and is controlled by a switch. The other coil, called the *secondary*, is attached to a light bulb. As long as the switch is closed and current flows, a magnetic field will exist around the primary coil. The secondary coil will come under its influence but nothing will happen yet.

Now suppose that the switch is opened. The current stops and the magnetic field around the primary coil can no longer exist. However, they do not simply disappear. The lines of force collapse or fall inward. As the lines fall inward, they wrap or cut across the loops in the secondary coil. That means that current is generated or induced in the secondary circuit. The light bulb will shine for a moment.

If the switch is closed, then opened again, the same thing will

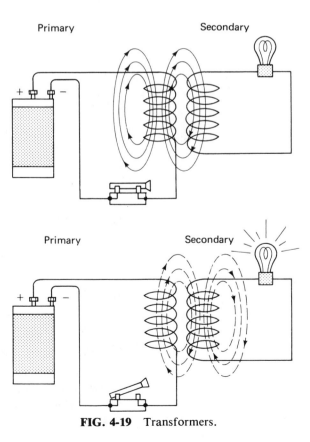

FIG. 4-19 Transformers.

happen. Every time the switch is opened, the collapsing lines of force from the primary will induce momentary current flow in the secondary.

This is the basic operating principle of the automotive ignition coil or any sort of transformer. In the ignition coil, the points (or some other form of "switch") periodically interrupt the current flow to induce the high-energy surges in the secondary needed to fire the spark plug. Power transformers use the periodic fluctions of ac current itself to induce current flow in secondary coils.

There is one more aspect of transformer operation you ought to realize. The basic function of a transformer, whether in an automobile coil or power generator, is to change voltage in a secondary circuit. This is done by altering the ratio between the number of turns of wire in the primary and secondary coils.

For instance, suppose that a primary coil has 10 loops and a secondary 100 loops (Fig. 4-20). Also, suppose that 20 A of ac current at 100 V passes through the primary. Since the secondary coil has 10 times as many loops, it will deliver 10 times as much voltage, or, in this case, 1,000 V. However, the amperage does not increase that way. It must be divided or spread out among the secondary loops, so it is reduced 10 times, to 2 A. The watts or power (volts and amps) is the same in both coils. The secondary coil has not created any extra energy, just rearranged it.

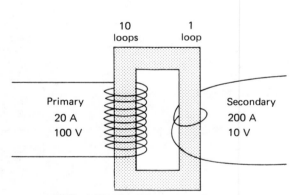

FIG. 4-20   Step-down transformer.

1. *If you have two side-by-side coils, one called the primary and one the secondary, and if the current to the primary coil is interrupted, what happens in the secondary circuit?*

2. *What functions are served by the points in the ignition coil?*

3. *What characteristic of ac current is used to induce current flow in the secondary of power company transformers?*

4. *What is the basic function of a transformer?*

5. *How is this function achieved?*

6. *What will be the output in a secondary coil given these conditions: primary coil, 100 turns; secondary coil, 100 turns; 5A of ac current at 10 V flowing in the primary?*

chapter

5

Starting Systems

INTRODUCTION The internal combustion engine (unlike the externally fired steam engine) cannot start itself. In the early days of the automobile, engines were cranked by hand. However, this was troublesome, unreliable, and often dangerous. So, in 1912, Charles F. Kettering invented the electric self-starter, or as it is more often called now, the *starting motor* or *cranking motor*. This chapter examines the starter motor, the cranking system of which it is a part, plus some fundamentals of electric motor operation.

BASIC CIRCUITRY The starter motor is part of the starting system, which, in turn, is part of the car's complete electrical system. Figure 5-1 shows some of the main elements in a simplified cranking system circuit: the battery, the start switch, a neutral safety switch, a cranking motor control switch, the cranking motor itself, and the necessary cables and wires to connect these components.

There are usually two main paths along which current may flow in a typical cranking system circuit. One path, represented by the heavy black lines, follows the thick cable running from the battery through the cranking motor control switch to the cranking motor.

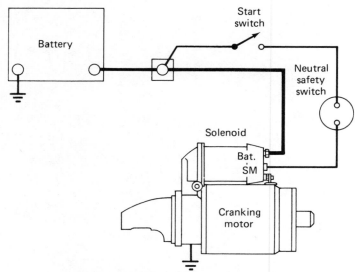

FIG. 5-1 Simplified cranking system circuit.

The other path follows the smaller wire from the start switch to the neutral safety switch and on to the cranking motor control switch.

The thick cable provides a low-resistance path for the heavy current flow required to operate the starter motor. The start switch and neutral safety switch *could* be included in this main operating circuit, but it would be dangerous. So the start and neutral safety switches are connected by high-resistance wires to reduce current flow and pressure.

The parallel branch in which the start and neutral safety switches are included is basically a signal or control circuit for the starter motor control switch. When the start and neutral safety switches are closed, current flows to the motor control. The current energizes an electromagnet which closes the starter motor control switch, which, in turn, allows current to flow along the heavy cable to the starter motor. Current continues to flow until the two signal switches are opened and the signal circuit is broken. Then the electromagnet breaks the main operating circuit to the starter motor.

1. *Name the main elements in a simplified cranking system circuit.*

2. *What are the two main paths along which current may flow in a typical cranking system circuit?*

3. *Why is it advisable to use a signal circuit as well as a main operating circuit?*

BASIC MECHANICAL COMPONENTS   The basic mechanical components of a simplified starter system are shown schematically in Fig. 5-2. There is a motor for supplying torque or turning force, a pinion or small gear attached to the motor's drive shaft, a flywheel ring gear, and a drive-engagement mechanism

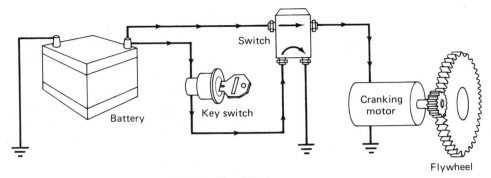

FIG. 5-2 Simplified starter system.

of some kind. The motor turns the pinion, which engages the flywheel ring gear, which turns the engine over. The drive engagement mechanism moves the pinion into mesh with the flywheel when the engine is being cranked and moves it out of mesh after the engine starts running.

1. Name the main components in a simplified starter system.

2. What is the purpose of the drive engagement mechanism?

3. When is the pinion brought into mesh with the flywheel, and when is it brought out of mesh?

ELECTRIC MOTORS

Review

Before starting this section on electric motors, it will be helpful to review some of the basic facts of magnetism introduced in Chapter 4.

1. Any wire or carrier of electricity is surrounded by lines of flux (actually three-dimensional flux "shells"). These force lines circle the wire in a direction determined by the direction of current flow through the wire.

2. Lines of force also act directionally in a permanent magnet, going from the north to the south pole, then circling back through the magnet to come out again at the north pole.

3. Magnetic flux lines moving in the same direction tend to join up and combine. Flux lines moving in opposite directions tend to push apart and separate.

4. If a wire carrying electric current is placed within a magnet's flux lines, the wire's own lines of force will try to join up with the magnet's flux lines on one side of their revolution around the wire and will try to separate on the other side of the wire. Consequently, the wire will move through the lines of force, repelled on one side and attracted on the other.

Basic operation

These basic principles explain the operation of almost any electric motor. To see how they apply, look at the simple motor shown in Fig. 5-3. The motor consists of two sets of windings. The inside windings, actually a single loop of wire in this simple illustration, are called the *armature*. It rotates within the stationary outside windings, called the *field*. The field winding is coiled around elements called *pole shoes*. The pole shoes are made of high-magnetic-permeability material. This helps concentrate and direct the lines of force in the field assembly.

Both the field and the armature produce magnetic flux lines when current flows through their windings. Considering one pole shoe as north and the other as south, the lines of force move from north to south in the field. In the armature, the flux lines circle in one direction on one side of the loop and in the other direction on the other side. That is because current flows in opposite directions as it travels down one side of the loop and back along the other side.

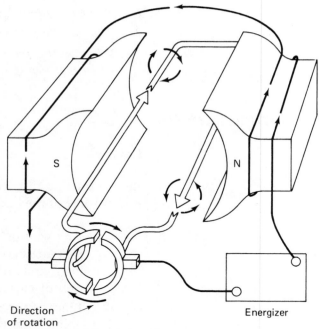

FIG. 5-3 Simple motor.

Because of the principles of magnetic attraction and repulsion noted in the preceding paragraphs, the armature loop will rotate within the field's flux lines. However, if you study Fig. 5-4, you will see that the armature can only rotate so far. When it is halfway between the poles, it reaches a position called the *static neutral point*. The magnetic forces balance one another and the armature will not rotate any further.

In order for the armature to continue its rotation, the current flow in the loop must be reversed (so the circling flux lines will also be

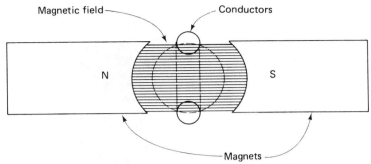

FIG. 5-4 Conductors at static neutral points.

reversed). This is accomplished by a split-ring commutator similar to the kind used in a dc generator. The ends of the armature loop are attached to the two halves of the commutator. Current enters and leaves the armature through a set of brushes that slide over the commutator sections. As the brushes pass from one commutator section to the other, the current flow in the armature is reversed, being pushed first through one side of the loop and then the other. If the brushes and commutator sections are properly placed, the current flow will be reversed just as the armature loop approaches the static neutral point.

In actual practice, a motor will be somewhat more complicated than the simple example described above. The armature will have a number of loops, each end attached to corresponding commutator sections. Also, the static neutral point will be shifted because of distortion in the field shoes' flux lines. The static neutral point (and as a result, the brushes) are moved back against the direction of armature rotation. Figure 5-5 shows a motor that is closer to those in actual use.

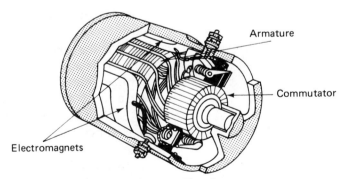

FIG. 5-5 Electric motor.

Electric motor construction

A typical starter motor contains field pole shoes and windings, the starter housing (or field frame), the armature assembly, the brushes, and plain bearing bushings supporting either end of the armature (Fig. 5-6).

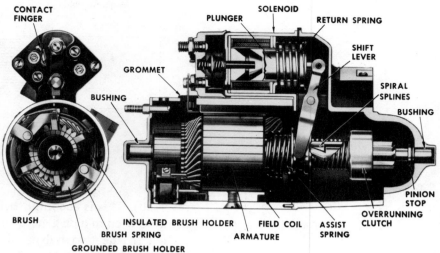

FIG. 5-6 Typical starter motor.

The pole shoes are constructed of soft iron for increased magnetic permeability. They are attached to the inside of the field frame by bevel-head screws.

The armature is also constructed from soft iron laminated with other materials for strength. Special slots are machined into the armature for the armature loops. The loops are made of heavy copper strips for reduced resistance.

The ends of the armature strips are attached to the commutator segments. The commutator is constructed of wedge-shaped copper pieces pressed into heat-resistant mica insulating material. The insulation separates the copper segments from one another and from the armature drive shaft, which passes through the center of the commutator. The commutator is machined to nearly perfect roundness on a lathe so that the brushes will follow true as the armature rotates.

The brushes are usually constructed of copper carbon compounds. Most starter motors have four brushes. Two are grounded to the frame or end plate and two are insulated from the frame.

Starter motor armatures are usually supported at either end by bronze-brass bushings. However, some heavy-duty motors have an extra, center bushing for added support.

Most starter motors are series-wound. In a typical example, current flows first (1) to the field windings, (2) then to the insulated brushes, (3) then through the commutator segment and the (4) armature winding contracting the brushes at that instant, (5) then out through the grounded brushes.

Performance characteristics

Starter motors use electromotive force (EMF) to operate. The torque and speed of the motor depend on the amount of current and the strength of the magnetic fields. The strength of the magnetic fields, in turn, is determined by the number of windings, the nature of the

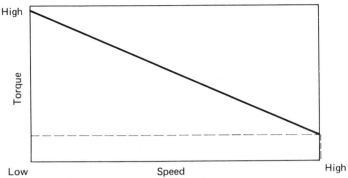

FIG. 5-7   Torque and speed relationship.

core material, and the amount of current flowing. The amount of current flowing depends on the supply of EMF from the battery and the resistance encountered in the motor circuits.

In series-wound motors, current flow and the resultant torque are greater at lower motor speeds (Fig. 5-7). This means that as the motor first starts to turn over, when the load is greatest, the current and torque will be high. Then as the motor speeds up, the current flow and torque will drop.

One of the reasons current falls off as the motor speeds up is the counterelectromotive force (CEMF) generated in the armature windings. As the armature rotates within the field's magnetic lines of force, and EMF is generated in the armature counter to the EMF from the battery. The motor, in effect, acts as a generator, inducing current flow as the armature windings cut across the field's flux lines. The motor reaches its maximum speed when the EMF from the battery is balanced by the resistance in the windings plus the CEMF from the armature.

The electric starter motor is a high-performance device. It produces considerable horsepower and torque under heavy loading. To reduce current flow and possible overheating, the motor is designed to operate at high speeds where current flow is least. For this reason, the gear ratio between the pinion and the flywheel ring gear is 15:1 to 20:1. In other words, the starter motor turns 15 to 20 times as fast as the engine. However, even with these precautions, the starter motor will overheat and suffer damage if allowed to operate much more than 30 seconds at one time.

Motor circuits

Most starter motors in use today have similar wiring circuits. Figure 5-8 shows a typical example. It has four pole shoes in the field assembly, two of which contain coils. The shoes wrapped with coils are both magnetic north and the unwrapped shoes, magnetic south. The field flux lines go out from the north poles, pass through the armature, go into the south poles, then return to the north poles through the field frame assembly. (Remember: magnetic lines of

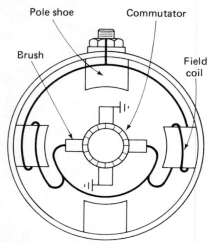

FIG. 5-8 Starter-motor wiring circuit: four-pole, two-coil.

force must follow a continuous flow path. Also, remember that flux lines *prefer* to pass through materials of high magnetic permeability—in this case, the iron shoes, armature, and field frame.)

The four-pole, two-coil motor just described acts in much the same way as a four-pole, four-coil motor, except that it offers less resistance to electrical flow, since there are fewer windings. This is one of the most common motor circuits. However, others are in use. There are four-coil, four-pole motors; motors with six coils wrapped around six poles; motors with a series-wound shunt coil to limit top speed; and others. Figure 5-9 shows some of these other motor configurations.

1. *What happens if a wire carrying electric current is placed within a magnet's flux lines?*

2. *What are the inside windings of a motor called?*

3. *What are the outside windings called?*

4. *What are the field windings coiled around?*

5. *What is the static neutral point?*

6. *What must happen for the armature to continue its rotation past the static neutral point?*

7. *What is the function of the commutator?*

8. *Why are the pole shoes constructed of soft iron?*

9. *Are starter motors usually series- or parallel-wound?*

10. *What is "EMF"?*

11. *What determines: the torque and speed of a motor? The strength of a motor's magnetic field? The current flow in a motor?*

12. *When are current flow and torque greatest in a series-wound motor?*

13. *How is CEMF generated in the armature windings of a motor as it speeds up?*

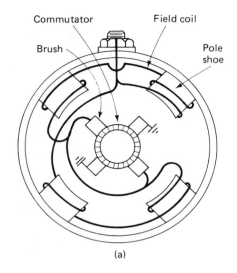

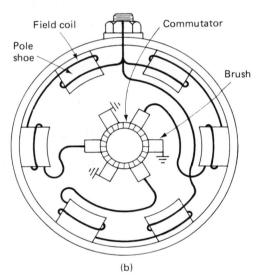

FIG. 5-9 Starter-motor wiring circuit: (a) four-pole, four-coil, (b) six-pole, six-coil.

14. *Why is the starter motor geared to operate so much faster than the engine?*

15. *How many pole shoes are there in the typical motor described in the preceding text? How many of these shoes are wrapped with coils?*

16. *Describe the path traveled by the flux lines from the field windings.*

FUNDAMENTAL OBSERVATIONS   If it were not for two fundamental facts, a cranking system need not be much more than a motor, start switch, pinion, and flywheel ring gear.

First, the heavy current required to operate the cranking motor (as much as 100 A) should not be routed directly through the start switch. As noted before, this might involve some danger, and the cables in the dash would have to be excessively large.

Second, the pinion cannot be allowed to remain engaged with the flywheel after the engine cranks. Given a gear ratio between the pinion and flywheel of 15 or 20:1, if they remained engaged after the engine was running at 1000 revolutions per minute (r/min), the starter motor would be driven by the engine at speeds of 15,000 to 20,000 r/min. The centrifugal forces at such speeds would quickly throw the windings out of the armature and destroy the motor.

It is because of these basic facts that the starting system requires some special features: a control circuit and associated switches, and a drive engagement mechanism to move the pinion in and out of mesh with the flywheel ring gear. The following sections describe these special features of the starting system.

1.   *What are the two factors that require special treatment in the starting system?*

2.   *What are these special features?*

STARTER DRIVES

There are two basic kinds of devices used to move the pinion in and out of mesh. One is the Bendix or inertia drive (and its several variations). The other is the overrunning clutch drive.

Bendix-type inertia drive

In standard-type Bendix drives, the pinion is fabricated around the outside of a hollow barrel (Fig. 5-10). The inside of the barrel has coarse-cut, screw threads. These threads are matched by similar threads on a sleeve assembly. The barrel is loosely threaded onto the sleeve and the sleeve is mounted onto the end of the armature drive shaft.

Torque from the armature is transmitted via a shock-absorbing spring and drive head to the sleeve. This causes the sleeve to rotate. However, at first, the barrel and pinion do not rotate with the sleeve.

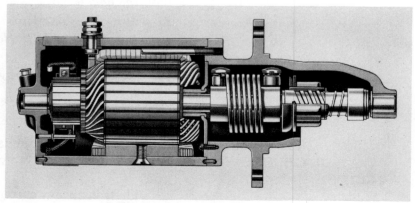

FIG. 5-10 Bendix-type inertia drive.

The loosely fitting barrel has a weight on one side to increase its inertia (the natural tendency of any object to resist change in velocity). So the sleeve rotates inside the barrel. As a result, the barrel screws itself down the length of the sleeve to the end, where it engages the flywheel gear. At that point, the barrel locks in place and begins to transmit torque from the armature. The so-called "Bendix spring" connecting the sleeve to the end of the armature shaft absorbs the engagement shock with the flywheel.

As soon as the engine starts running on its own, it will rotate faster than the armature. This causes the pinion to be screwed back down the sleeve and out of mesh with the flywheel. Should the pinion be driven back down with excessive force, a small overrunning clutch is activated to prevent damage to the starter motor.

Bendix barrel-type drive

The barrel drive is similar to the standard Bendix-type drive. The principal differences are these: the pinion is usually mounted on the end of the barrel; it is generally smaller (for higher gear ratios) and it works directly off screw threads at the end of the armature shaft instead of through an intervening sleeve assembly (Fig. 5-11).

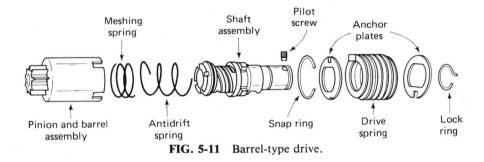

FIG. 5-11   Barrel-type drive.

Bendix folo-thru drives

The folo-thru drive is similar to the Bendix barrel drive. The principal differences are the addition of a "detent" pin and a "detent" clutch (Fig. 5-12).

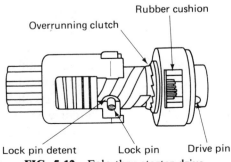

FIG. 5-12   Folo-thru starter drive.

The detent pin locks the barrel in place on the screwshaft. This locking action takes place after the pinion barrel has moved to the end of the screw shaft, when the shaft is turning rapidly. Centrifugal force throws the pin into engagement between the barrel and the screwshaft.

The detent clutch connects the two sections of the screwshaft. If the engine should run faster than the armature shaft, the clutch disengages, thus protecting the motor from damage.

Inboard or outboard drives

In many Bendix drives the pinion is screwed "outward" from the motor to engage the flywheel. These are called "outboard" drives. In other cases the pinion is driven inward toward the motor. This is called an "inboard" drive.

Overrunning clutch drive

The overrunning clutch drive operates on an entirely different principle from Bendix-type drives (Fig. 5-13). Instead of using an inertia operated screw to move the pinion in and out of mesh with the flywheel ring gear, the pinion is moved by a shift linkage of some kind. In fact, the overrunning clutch itself might not be considered the most important element in this kind of drive. The control element that operates the pinion shift linkage could be considered more important, since it actually moves the pinion into mesh with the flywheel.

The overrunning clutch, like the clutch in the folo-thru drive is primarily a safety device separating the armature drive shaft from the pinion. A sleeve and hollow shell assembly make up one-half of the clutch. They are splined onto the armature drive shaft. The pinion and a collar comprise the other half of the clutch. The pinion is mounted onto the collar, which fits inside the shell.

Positive engagement between the collar and the shell is provided by spring-loaded rollers located in slots within the shell. When the armature is turning more slowly than the engine, the rollers jam into contact with the sleeve, causing the connected pinion to transmit torque to the engine. But when the engine runs faster than the armature, the rollers are driven up their ramps to the wider side of the slots. Then the rollers act as bearings so that the collar can spin freely inside the shell, and in so doing not transmit any damaging torque back to the motor.

Some overrunning clutch drives use a system of oval-shaped rollers called "sprags." These sprags rock back and forth into engagement with the pinion collar.

The shift linkage used to move the pinion in and out of engagement with the flywheel ring gear may be manually operated or controlled by an electric solenoid. Most starters today use the solenoid control. It will be described presently.

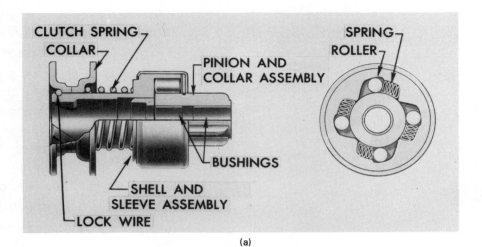

(a)

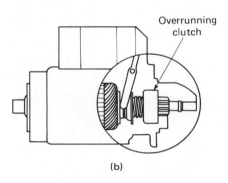

(b)

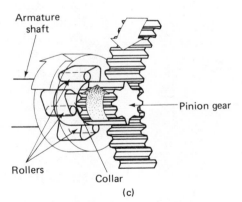

(c)

FIG. 5-13 Overrunning clutch.

Dyer drives

Dyer drives are often used in heavy-duty truck or industrial applications. They combine features of both Bendix type and overrunning clutch drives. Like the overrunning clutch drive, the pinion is meshed with the flywheel by a shift lever. And like the inertia drive, the pinion is spun out of mesh along screw threads once the engine operates faster than the starter motor.

1. *What are the two basic kinds of devices used to move the pinion in and out of mesh with the flywheel?*

2. *Where is the pinion located in a standard Bendix-type drive?*

3. *In this kind of drive, does the pinion begin rotation the same time as the sleeve, and if not, why not?*

4. *What causes the pinion to disengage from the ring gear after the engine cranks?*

5. *How is a Bendix barrel-type drive different from the standard Bendix drive?*

6. *In what ways are the Bendix folo-thru drive different?*

7. *What is the difference between inboard and outboard drives?*

8. *How is the pinion in an overrunning clutch drive moved back and forth?*

9. *The overrunning clutch itself serves what principal function?*

10. *What provides positive engagement between the shell and the pinion collar?*

11. *What happens to the rollers when the engine runs faster than the armature?*

12. *How is a dyer drive like an overrunning clutch drive and a Bendix drive?*

CONTROL SWITCHES

The switches that control the flow of high-amperage current to the starter motor should not be considered apart from the starter drive. Bendix-type drives almost always employ a magnetic switch. And overrunning clutch drives generally use a solenoid switch to control current flow as well as to move the pinion in and out of mesh with the flywheel ring gear.

Both magnetic switches and solenoids operate on the principle introduced earlier. That is, loops of wire wrapped around a hollow core will draw a plunger into that core when the loops carry electric current.

Magnetic switches

Magnetic switches used in Bendix-type drives consist primarily of a coil, a plunger with a disk connected at one end, and electrical contacts attached to the main operating circuit (Fig. 5-14). The switch may be located in any convenient place along the main operating circuit cable.

When the operator turns the start switch to a closed position, the signal circuit sends current to the magnetic switch windings. This creates a magnetic field around the windings. The magnetic field pulls the plunger inside the coil. When the plunger moves, the contact disc on the end joins the contacts on the two sides of the main operating circuit. High-amperage current then flows through the disc and contacts to the starter motor.

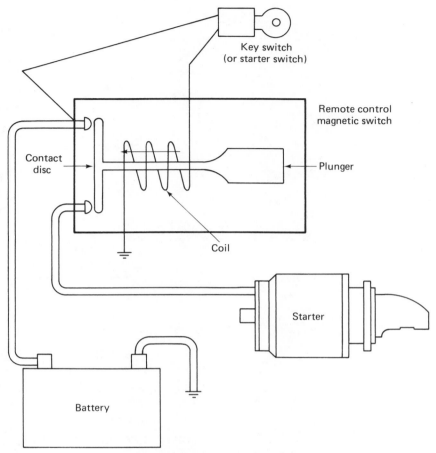

FIG. 5-14 Magnetic switch.

As long as the operator holds the switch key in the crank position, the magnetic switch windings will remain energized, and the main operating circuit will allow current to flow to the starter motor. However, when the operator releases the switch, the signal circuit will be broken and the magnetic field will collapse. Then, the spring-loaded plunger will move the contact disk away from the main circuit contacts, breaking that circuit and turning the starter motor off.

Solenoid switch

The plunger in the solenoid switch has two jobs. It must close the main operating circuit so that current will flow to the starter motor. It must also operate the shift linkage which moves the pinion in and out of mesh. (Remember: the solenoid is used primarily with overrunning clutch drives.)

To do these two jobs, two sets of windings are required. One, the pull-in winding, has the heavy-duty job of shifting the pinion into mesh. The other, the hold-in winding, holds the plunger disc against the main circuit contacts after the pinion has engaged. The pull-in winding is fabricated from heavy wire to reduce resistance and pro-

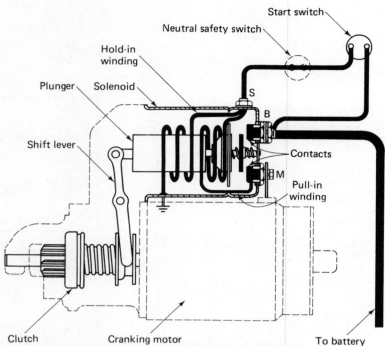

FIG. 5-15 Circuits and operation of a typical solenoid switch.

duces the strongest field. The hold-in winding has more turns of finer wire.

Figure 5-15 illustrates the circuits and operation of a typical solenoid. When the start and neutral safety switches are closed, current flows from the battery along the main circuit cable to terminal B. Then the current flows through the start and neutral safety switches to terminal S. From that switch, current goes to the pull-in and hold-in windings. The combined fields of these two windings pull the plunger inside the solenoid's hollow core.

Two things happen when the plunger moves inside the core. The shift lever at one end of the plunger pushes the pinion into mesh with the flywheel gear. At the other end of the plunger, a disc attached to the plunger is pushed against the contacts at terminals B and M. Now the battery current can flow from terminal B through the disc, to terminal M, and on to the cranking motor.

However, something else also happens when the disc closes the circuit branch between terminals B and M. To understand this, notice that the hold-in windings are grounded through the cranking motor frame, whereas the pull-in windings are grounded through terminal M to the motor. This means that when the disc connects terminals B and M, the electrical path between the terminals is shorter through the disc than through the hold-in windings. So the disc, in effect, shorts out the pull-in windings and reduces the power of its field. This is an economy measure to increase current flow to the motor during cranking. The power of the hold-in windings is sufficient to maintain contact across terminals B and M.

When the start switch is allowed to open, all the circuits are broken and the magnetic field around the hold-in windings begins to collapse. As it falls inward, it cuts across the pull-in windings. This creates a momentary current flow in the opposite direction, which, in turn, creates an opposite acting magnetic field around the pull-in windings. This field neutralizes what is left of the hold-in field so that the heavy-duty plunger return spring can quickly pull the pinion out of mesh with the flywheel.

1. *Starter system control switches should not be considered apart from what?*
2. *What kind of control do Bendix-type drives most often use?*
3. *What kind of control do overrunning clutch drives most often use?*
4. *What are the basic components in a Bendix magnetic switch?*
5. *What happens to the plunger when the operator turns the ignition switch on?*
6. *The contact disc on the end of the plunger joins the two sides of which circuit?*
7. *What are the two jobs of the plunger in the solenoid switch?*
8. *What is the job of the hold-in winding, and what is the job of the pull-in winding?*
9. *Go back to the text and trace, once again, the operation of the solenoid switch.*

chapter
6

Transistors
and Semiconductors

INTRODUCTION   In 1956, the Nobel prize for physics was awarded to three American researchers: Bardeen, Brittain, and Shockley. The first two men invented the transistor and the third, Shockley, explained the physical principles involved. Before that, few people outside the scientific community appreciated the importance of what had been done. Since then, transistors and other semiconductors have been used in everything from portable radios to Apollo moon rockets. Semiconducting devices have also found their way into automotive applications. All alternating charging systems use them, as well as most ignition systems.

In order to understand automotive systems based on semiconductors, it is necessary to appreciate some of the theory involved. This chapter will introduce you to the subject.

ATOMIC STRUCTURE   *Semiconductors*, as a category of matter, fall somewhere between conductors and nonconductors. The differences are primarily due to the number and arrangement of electrons and to the way atoms are joined. The structure of a conductor promotes electrical flow, whereas the bonding between atoms of nonconductors inhibits current movement. Semiconductors may be either conductors or nonconductors, depending on certain circumstances and on the presence of carefully introduced impurities. This "either–or" property of semiconductors makes them valuable as one-way current valves, electrical switches, and so on. To see how semiconductors work, it will be necessary to look again at atomic structure, paying particular attention this time to the behavior of outer-shell electrons.

Reviewing from the beginning: all matter is composed of atoms (Fig. 6-1). Atoms, in turn, are composed of electrons, protons, and

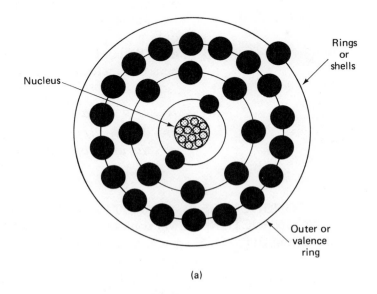

(a)

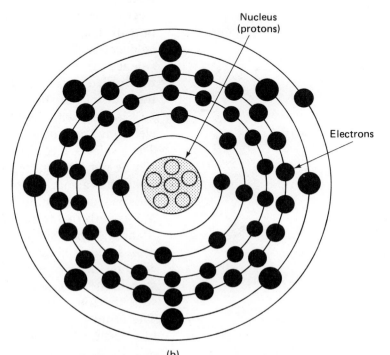

(b)

FIG. 6-1 (a) Atomic nomenclature. (b) Uranium atom.

neutrons. Positively charged protons and no-charge neutrons occupy the nucleus of atoms. Negatively charged electrons move in circular orbits around the nucleus, much the same way that planets orbit the sun in our solar system. Current flow is a movement of these electrons from one atom to another under the influence of an EMF.

Electrons occupy different orbits or shells around the nucleus. Following a definite pattern, some electrons orbit close to the nucleus and some orbit farther away. The number of electrons in any given orbit depends on the position of the orbit (first, second, third, etc.).

The electrons in the inner orbits are tightly bound to the nucleus. As a rule they do not enter into reactions with the electrons from other atoms. However, this is not the case with electrons in the outermost or valence orbits. The number of electrons in the valence orbit determines the electrical nature of a substance, whether it will be a conductor of electricity, a nonconductor, or a semiconductor.

1. *As a category of matter, where do semiconductors fall?*
2. *Which electrons determine the electrical nature of a substance, the inner-orbit electrons or the valence-orbit electrons?*

CONDUCTORS, NONCONDUCTORS, AND SEMICONDUCTORS

An "ideal" valence orbit contains eight electrons. No valence orbit will contain more than eight, but many will have less. When that happens, an atom will try to "lend" or "borrow" electrons to achieve the satisfied state.

Atoms with one to three valence electrons tend to "lend" electrons [Fig. 6-2(a)]. They are conductors of electricity. Their valence electrons are rather loosely held and with a sufficient application of outside energy can be put into motion. For instance, the single valence electron of a copper atom can be easily made to drift to the valence orbit of the next copper atom. Then its valence electron will be repelled to the next atom, and so on. The result is electron movement or current flow.

Atoms with five to seven valence electrons tend to "borrow" electrons from other atoms [Fig. 6-2(b)]. They are nonconductors. Their valence electrons are more tightly held to the nucleus and cannot be put into motion easily.

The valence orbits of two or more atoms combine to achieve the satisfied valence state. Atoms with one to three valence electrons join atoms with five to seven valence electrons (by the "borrowing" and "lending" process), so the total valence electrons of the combined atoms equals eight [Fig. 6-2(c)]. Atoms with four valence electrons combine with one another to achieve the ideal condition. For instance, the four valence electrons of a germanium atom can combine with the four valence electrons of a neighboring germanium atom. The result is a complex, lattice-work crystal of satisfied valence orbits, each having eight electrons [Fig. 6-2(d)].

Because of this structure, atoms with four valence electrons are called semiconductors. In their pure state, considerable voltage or

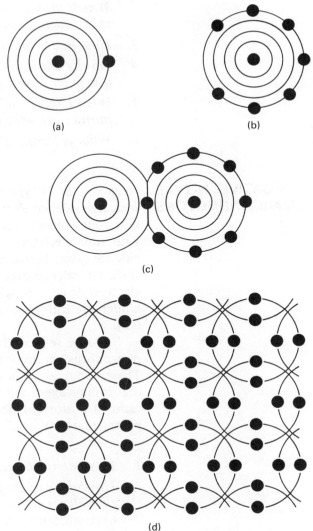

FIG. 6-2 Atoms with valence electrons. (a) Atom with one valence electron. (b) Atom with seven valence electrons. (c) "Shared" valence electrons to achieve "balanced" eight-electron valence orbit. (d) Crystal lattice work of semiconductor atoms. Neighboring atoms share four valence electrons to achieve balanced valence orbits.

high temperatures are required to break loose electrons from the satisfied valence combinations. However, something dramatic happens to the conductivity of semiconductors when impurities are added. Depending on the kind of impurity, a semiconductor can be made into a carrier of negative charges or positively charged "holes." The process is called *doping* and the result is a conducting semiconductor. The remainder of this chapter will examine the formation and behavior of semiconductors.

1. *Whose valence electrons can be put into motion most easily, atoms with one to three valence electrons or atoms with five to seven valence electrons?*

2. *Which atoms are conductors of electricity, those with one to three valence electrons or those with five to seven?*

3. *How many valence electrons does a semiconductor have?*

4. *Do the atoms of a semiconductor have to combine with other, dissimilar atoms to achieve the satisfied valence state?*

5. *What happens to the conductivity of a semiconductor when impurities are added?*

6. *What is "doping"?*

NEGATIVE, N-TYPE SEMICONDUCTORS

Negative, or N-type semiconductors are created by adding atoms with five valence electrons to the parent material (whose atoms contain four valence electrons). Four of the added electrons combine with four electrons of a parent atom to form a stable, combined valence orbit. However, the fifth added electron has no where to go since no valence orbit can contain more than eight electrons. This electron drifts through the lattice structure of the combined atoms. Under the influence of an EMF, it will support current flow (Fig. 6-3).

N-type semiconductors are created by adding materials such as phosphorus, antimony, and arsenic to the parent, semiconductor. These additives are sometimes called N-type doping agents. Usually, the doping agent is combined with the parent semiconductor at a ratio of 1 atom of doping agent for every 10 million atoms of the parent material.

1. *How many valence electrons do N-type doping agents contain?*

2. *How many of the doping agent's valence electrons combine with the valence electrons of the parent atoms, and how many are left uncombined to drift free?*

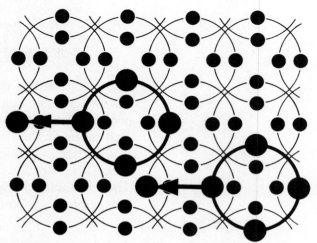

FIG. 6-3 N-doped semiconductor. Extra electrons support current flow in the presence of EMF.

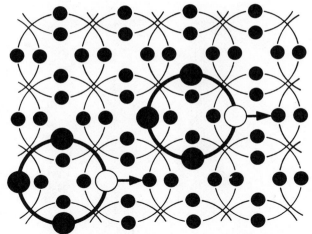

FIG. 6-4 P-doped semiconductor. Missing valence electron creates a "positive hole" which will support current flow.

POSITIVE, P-TYPE SEMICONDUCTORS

Positive or P-type semiconductors are created by adding atoms with three electrons in their valence orbits (aluminum, indium, boron). These atoms, as before, enter the lattice structure of the parent semiconductor. However, this time, electrons are missing from the valence orbits of the combined atoms. Some of the valence orbits will only have seven electrons instead of eight. The empty spaces in P-type semiconductors are considered to be positively charged "holes" (Fig. 6-4) because the "unsatisfied" valence orbits will have a tendency to attract free electrons into the holes, the same as if an actual positively charged particle were present.

1.   *How many valence electrons do P-type doping agents have?*

2.   *What do you call the empty spaces in the valence orbits of P-type semiconductors?*

3.   *What kind of charge are these empty spaces said to possess?*

CURRENT THEORY: ELECTRON VERSUS HOLE MOVEMENT

In order to understand semiconductor operation, it is necessary to add to the previously described theory of current flow. Going back to the example of a copper wire attached to the positive and negative terminals of a battery, we have said that the absence of electrons at the positive terminal tends to pull electrons out of the wire and that the excess of electrons at the negative terminal pushes electrons back in to replace those pulled out. The pulling action is due to magnetic attraction between unlike charges, and the pushing action is due to magnetic repulsion between like charges.

If we include the valence theory introduced in this chapter, we can go on to say that the positive terminal attracts the nearest copper atom's single-valence electrons. This attractive force gives the electrons sufficient energy to move from the so-called valence energy

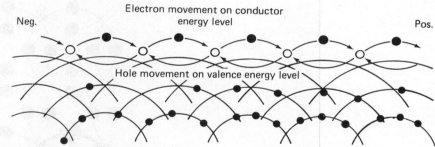

FIG. 6-5 Whenever an electron goes up to the conductor level, it leaves a hole behind. This hole attracts a neighboring electron which leaves a hole behind which attracts another electron, and so on. The result is current flow.

level up to the conductor level (Fig. 6-5). At this energy level, the electrons become free, able to drift under the influence of an EMF toward the battery's positive terminal.

However, something else happens when an electron moves up the conductor level. It leaves behind an empty space or hole in the valence orbit. Since this hole will attempt to capture an electron, it is considered to be positively charged. It will attract negatively charged electrons.

When a shifting electron creates a positive hole, the hole has a tendency to fill itself by attracting another electron from a neighbor atom. Then, when that electron is excited out of its valence energy level another hole is created. That hole attracts another electron, which creates another hole, which attracts another electron, which creates another hole, and so on. Consequently, as electrons move from the negative to the positive side of the circuit along the conductor level, positive holes will move along the valence level from positive to negative. This means that current flow can actually be described in two ways: as the movement of negative electrons and positive holes.

In the early days of automotive engineering, current flow was usually said to flow from positive to negative (although it wasn't explained in terms of "holes"). Now, most experts say that current moves from negative to positive. To explain diode and transistor operation, both negative and positive flow concepts are needed.

1. What does an electron leave behind when it moves from the valence energy level to the conductor level?

2. What is the direction of positively charged hole movement?

3. Why do we need both positive and negative current flow concepts?

CURRENT FLOW IN N- AND P-TYPE SEMICONDUCTORS

Both N- and P-type semiconductors will support current flow (Fig. 6-6). In N-type semiconductors, current flow depends primarily on the movement of free electrons contributed by the doping agent. When a source of EMF is connected to an N-type conductor, the

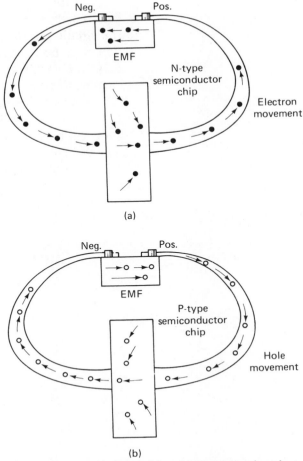

FIG. 6-6 P- and N-doped chips. (a) N-type semiconductor in the presence of an EMF. (b) P-type semiconductor in the presence of an EMF.

negative side of the circuit pushes electrons through the semiconductor and the positive side attracts the free electrons. [Fig. 6-6(a)].

In P-type semiconductors, current flow depends primarily on the empty holes formed by the doping agent. When P-type material is attached to an EMF, the negative side of the circuit attracts the positive charged holes and the positive side repels the holes [Fig. 6-6(b)].

1. What carries the current in N-type semiconductors?

2. What carries the current in P-type semiconductors?

DIODES In most automotive applications, semiconductors are not used singly. They are combined in two or three layers to form diodes or transistors.

N- and P-type semiconductors joined in thin, two-layer chips are called *diodes*. Diodes are used to change or rectify ac to dc current, and with special types of diodes to help control the voltage output of alternators.

There are two basic ways a diode may be introduced into a circuit. The N half of the diode may be connected to the negative side of the circuit and the P half to the positive side [Fig. 6-7(a)]. Or, the N half may be connected to positive and the P half to negative [Fig. 6-7(c)]. Depending on how the diode is connected, it will either allow current to flow or it will act as a barrier to electron movement.

One key to understanding diode (and later, transistor) operation is to examine the behavior of positive and negative charges at the junction between P- and N-type layers.

When a diode is not attached to a circuit [Fig. 6-7(b)], the positive holes from the P side and the negative charges from the N

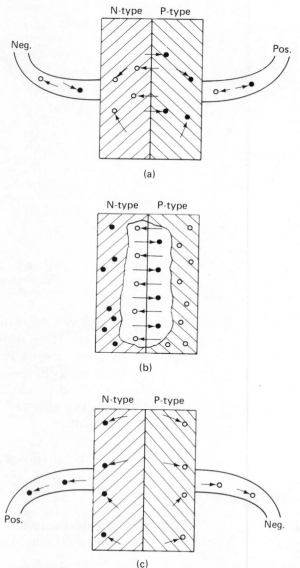

(a)

(b)

(c)

FIG. 6-7 Diodes. (a) Forward-biased diode (current flow). Electrons and holes cross P/N junction. (b) Unconnected diode. Internal EMF due to cross over at junction. (c) Reverse-biased diode (no current flow). Electrons and holes pulled from junction. There is no crossover.

side are drawn toward the junction. Some charges cross over to combine with opposite charges from the other side. However, when the charges cross over, the two diode halves are no longer electrically balanced. In other words, when an electron from the N side goes over to the P side, it leaves a positive charge behind on the N side. The same kind of thing happens when a hole goes from P to N. Consequently, each half of the diode builds up a network of internal charges opposite to the charges at the PN junction. The attraction (or internal EMF) between the opposite charges tends to limit further diffusion of charges across the junction.

When the diode is attached to an external EMF source, the situation changes. If the diode is connected P to positive and N to negative, there will be current flow. The negative pole will push electrons across the barrier as the positive pole pushes holes across. The diode is said to be forward-biased.

However, if the diode is attached P side to the negative pole and N side to positive, there will be no current flow. The negative pole will attract the positive holes away from the junction and the positive pole will attract the electrons away. As a result, no charges will cross over the junction. The diode is then said to be reverse-biased. These features give the diode the ability to act as an ac to dc rectifier or as a one-way current valve.

1. *How many layers do diodes have?*

2. *What are the two basic ways a diode may be introduced into a circuit?*

3. *When a diode is* not *attached to a circuit, where do the positive and negative charges tend to go?*

4. *What happens to the electrical balance of the two diode halves when charges cross over at the PN Junction?*

5. *After the initial crossover of charges at the PN junction, what prevents further charge crossover?*

6. *When a diode is connected to a circuit, P side to positive and N side to negative, what happens at the PN junction? Will this action prevent or promote current flow? And is the diode said to be forward- or reverse-biased?*

7. *When a diode is connected P side to negative and N side to positive, what happens at the PN junction? Will this action prevent or promote current flow and is the diode said to be forward- or reverse-biased?*

SEMICONDUCTOR BREAKDOWN/ZENER DIODES

Most charge movement or current flow in a diode is the result of the impurities added to the parent semiconductor. It is called extrinsic flow because it is external to or apart from the basic atomic structure of the pure semiconductor. It depends on the extra electrons or holes added by the impurity.

Current flow that depends on the electrons provided by the parent semiconductor itself is called *intrinsic flow* because it is intrinsic or basic to the parent material. Intrinsic flow in most semiconductors is limited to the few electrons that can slip along the atomic cracks and flaws within the crystal structure of the parent material. In other words, these few electrons find pathways through the otherwise satisfied crystal network.

Intrinsic flow in semiconductors increases as the temperature goes up (as opposed to metal conductivity, which increases as the temperature goes down). In most cases, the intrinsic current flow in semiconductors does not become significant until the material nears its melting point—when the atoms are vibrating so much that the valence bonds are about to break apart. However, certain carefully prepared, heavily doped semiconductors can be made to conduct intrinsic current at lower temperatures.

Note: The temperature of semiconductors is raised by increasing the voltage impressed against it. The greater the voltage the greater the force given to electrons moving between atoms and the more the atoms will vibrate. Heat is the result of atomic vibration.

Zener diodes are constructed from semiconductors which will allow intrinsic current flow above certain voltage/heat levels. Below these levels, a Zener diode behaves in a normal manner, allowing only extrinsic, forward-biased current to pass. However, when sufficient, reverse-biased voltage is applied, the diode will "break down" and allow intrinsic current to pass in the opposite direction. Zener diodes are particularly useful in voltage-regulating devices and as protective shunt switches for other circuit components, usually transistors.

1.   *What additions to the parent semiconductor provide the charges for extrinsic flow?*

2.   *What features in undoped semiconductors provide the basis for intrinsic flow?*

3.   *How is the temperature of a semiconductor raised to increase its current-carrying capacity?*

4.   *What will happen in a normal semiconductor before the temperature reaches a conducting level?*

5.   *How are Zener diodes different?*

6.   *What are some applications for Zener diodes?*

TRANSISTORS

Transistors are three-layer semiconducting chips. The two principal combinations are NPN and PNP. In effect, a transistor is made up of two diodes, each sharing a center layer. No matter how the transistor is connected into a circuit, one of the diodes will be reversed-biased and the other forward-biased.

The three layers in a transistor have certain designations. The

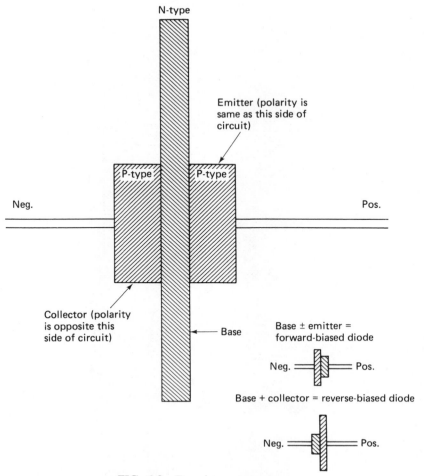

FIG. 6-8 Transistor components.

outside layer of the forward-biased diode (the layer whose polarity is the same as the polarity of the circuit side to which it is attached) is called the *emitter* (Fig. 6-8). The outside layer of the reversed bias diode is called the *collector*. The shared center layer is called the *base*. Each layer—emitter, collector, and base—has its own electrical lead for connecting to different parts of a circuit.

Common materials used for the emitter and the collector are germanium, N doped with phosphorus and P doped with boron. The base section, also commonly made from germanium, is usually only lightly doped, just enough to give a certain minimal number of free charges. The base is very thin compared to the other layers. And its lead is usually attached to a surrounding ring somewhat removed from the emitter/base/collector junctions.

The base section provides a key to transistor operation. To see how it works, examine Fig. 6-9. Figure 6-9(a) diagrams a PNP transistor with the lead from its base layer connected to an open circuit leg (which removes the base section from a source of charges). The positive holes in the P-type collector are pushed by the positive charges in the attached circuit to the junction between the collector and the base. On the other side of the transistor, magnetic attraction

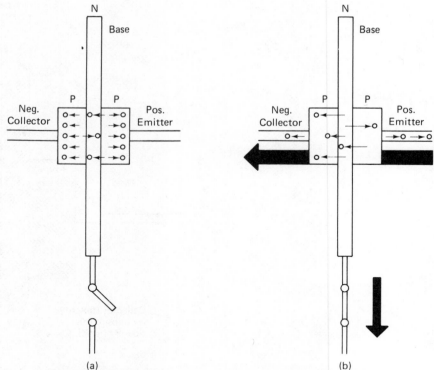

FIG. 6-9 Transistor operation. (a) Base circuit open: no current flow from emitter to collector. (b) Base circuit closed: current flow from emitter to collector. There is a much larger current flow through the emitter/collector than through the base.

draws the positive holes in the collector away from the collector base junction. Many (of the already limited number) of free electrons in the base section are drawn to the emitter/base junction. As a result of this counterbalancing arrangement of charges, few positive or negative charges can pass completely across the base layer. The base layer does not have enough electrons to support any thing more than a minor current "leakage" through the layers. And the transistor assumes the character of the reverse-biased diode pair.

Current will only flow when the base circuit is completed [Fig. 6-9(b)]. Then it provides sufficient electrons to support hole movement from the emitter across the base to the collector. However, the amount of current flowing through the layers is different. Because the base layer is so thin and because the base circuit is attached to a ring relatively removed from the emitter/base junction, the holes speeding out of the emitter can pass more easily into the collector. Only a limited number of holes will go from the emitter through the base.

The base circuit acts as a control for the emitter/collector circuits. When the base circuit is open, no current passes; and when it is closed, current flows. And because few charges are allowed to pass through the base, a limited amount of current flow in the base can be used to control much heavier current flows in the emitter circuit. This is practically useful in the operation of certain transistorized ignition systems, where it is desirable to keep the current flow through the ignition points as low as possible.

1. *How many layers do transistors have?*

    A transistor, in effect, is made up of two diodes, one forward-biased and one reversed-biased. What do you call the outside layer of the forward-biased diode? Also, what do you call the outside layer of the negative diode and what do you call the shared center section?

3. *Is the base layer usually thick or thin compared to the other two layers?*

4. *When the circuit leg attached to the base layer is open, will current flow through the emitter and collector?*

5. *When a transistor is operating, how much current flows through the base compared to the amount flowing through the emitter and collector?*

chapter

7

Charging Systems

INTRODUCTION A storage battery, operating alone, cannot supply an automobile's electrical needs for an extended period of time. Besides the engine, the radio, lights, windshield wiper, lighter, and horn all require electrical power. To keep these systems functioning, automobiles must have a charging device.

The charger is operated by a V-belt connected to a pulley on the end of the crankshaft. In effect, the charger converts some of the crankshaft's mechanical energy (which was derived from the fuel's chemical energy) into electrical energy. This energy is used to charge the battery as well as to supply the needs of the other electrical devices.

There are two basic kinds of chargers, the generator and the alternator. The operating principles of both are similar. However, generators are no longer used on most modern cars. So this chapter will deal only briefly with generators and will concentrate on alternators.

CHARGER-BATTERY Before getting into an explanation of either chargers or alternators, it
RELATIONSHIP will be helpful to explore briefly the relationship between the charging device and the battery.

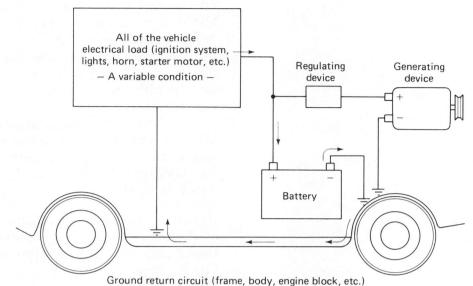

Ground return circuit (frame, body, engine block, etc.)
FIG. 7-1 When the engine is first started, the battery supplies the vehicle's electrical needs.

When a vehicle is first started, before the charger is rotating very fast, the battery supplies all the vehicle's electrical needs. As noted in Fig. 7-1, electrons move out of the battery negative post, through the ground return circuit, to the vehicle's electrical load elements, and then back to the positive battery terminal to form a complete circuit. A regulating device of some kind prevents the battery from discharging back into the charger at these speeds.

After the battery has operated for a time, its ability to produce current will be reduced. Also, as the engine speeds up, the charger, because of is basic design, will be able to produce more voltage than the battery can deliver, even when it is fully charged (Fig. 7-2). So

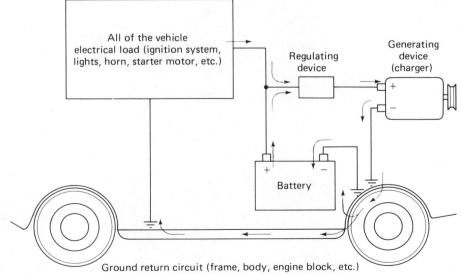

Ground return circuit (frame, body, engine block, etc.)
FIG. 7-2 At higher speeds the charger pushes verse charging current through the battery as well as supplies vehicle load.

electrons from the charger, as they move into the ground circuit, are able to move in a reverse direction through the battery's negative terminal. In other words, the charger's EMF will be able to overcome the battery's CEMF. As illustrated in Fig. 7-2, the charger supplies the vehicle's load requirements as well as pushes reverse current through the battery. The reverse current builds up and maintains the battery's charge level.

If the vehicle's electrical load increases sufficiently, or if the load increases while the vehicle slows down, the charger's voltage output may drop very near the battery's output. At these times, both the battery and the charger supply current to satisfy the vehicle's load. This is illustrated in Fig. 7-3.

Note: As indicated in Chapter 6, current flow can be described as electrons moving from negative to positive or as "holes" going from positive to negative. Most authorities now describe current as flowing from negative to positive, because it fits more easily into the concept of electron movement. This book has also followed that practice. You should be aware, however, that some books and materials, including this one on occasion, will, where it is more convenient, indicate that current goes from positive to negative. It does not make any difference as far as the operation of a particular device is concerned—although you may be confused, unless you remember that both ways are correct as long as you don't mix them up.

1. *Which electrical supply source, the battery or the charger, supplies the electrical load when a vehicle is first started?*

2. *After the vehicle is at operating speed, and without any unusual load being present, the charger supplies current for two main areas. What are they?*

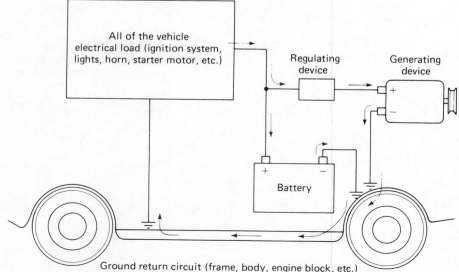

FIG. 7-3 A combination of heavier electrical load and lower operating speed will reduce charger output near battery potential so that both must supply current.

3. *Describe the path taken by electrons through the battery when it is being recharged by the charger.*

4. *What happens, when, because of load or a drop in speed, the charger's output falls to a level near the battery output?*

5. *Why do you think it is important to bear in mind the difference between the two descriptions of current flow?*

GENERATORS

BASIC PRINCIPLES As indicated in previous chapters, whenever there is relative movement between a conductor and magnetic lines of force, the electrical balance of the conductor's atoms will be upset. As the lines of force cut through the conductor's atomic structure, electron movement or current flow results.

The lines of force can be supplied by a permanent magnet or an electromagnet. However, since it is difficult to adjust the output of a permanent magnet (which is necessary to control voltage and current output), all automotive chargers use electromagnets.

In a generator there are two sets of windings: an outside stationary set, called the *field*, and an inside rotating set, called the *armature*. The field windings make up the electromagnet. When current passes through the field windings, magnetic lines of force circle around and through the field shoes and frame.

The interior, armature windings are mounted on a shaft connected to the generator drive pulley (Fig. 7-4). When rotated by this pulley, the armature windings cut across the lines of force circling the field. As a result, electrons are put into motion in the armature windings. These electrons travel from the armature through the com-

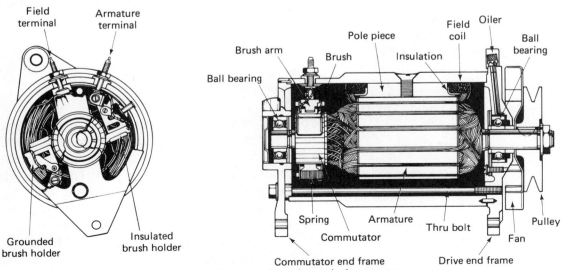

FIG. 7-4 Cross section of a typical generator.

mutator segments to the brushes. Then the current goes to the battery and the rest of the car's electrical system, eventually returning to the generator to form a complete circuit.

The output from the armature windings is controlled by varying the magnetic strength of the field windings. The magnetic strength of the field windings is controlled by varying the current flowing into the field.

1. *What are the two ways lines of magnetic force can be supplied for a generating device, and which is the best way for automobiles?*
2. *In a generator, what do you call the outside stationary set of windings, and what do you call the inside rotating set?*
3. *Which set of windings makes up the electromagnet?*
4. *Which set of windings cuts through the magnetic lines of force to yield current flow?*
5. *How is the armature output controlled?*

GENERATOR CONSTRUCTION

The basic components inside the generator housing or frame are the stationary field windings, the rotating armature windings, the brushes, and the commutator. As you may have noticed, these are the same basic components of an electric motor, such as like the starter motor studied in Chapter 5. And as you may have guessed, a generator can actually function as a motor.

The construction of a generator and a motor are not identical, but for the purposes of this limited discussion, you can refer back to the introductory section to get a general idea of basic generator construction.

1. *What are the basic components of a generator?*

OPERATING FEATURES

Shunt-wound/self-excited

Most electric motors are *series-wound*, meaning that the current goes from the field windings to the armature windings with no intervening branches. Most generators, however, are *parallel-wound*, or as it is often called, shunt-wound (Fig. 7-5). This means that the field windings are branched off from the armature windings.

The current used to operate the field is taken (via a regulating device) from the armature's output. Such a process is called *self-excitation*. A self-exciting generator can, in theory, produce current without being attached to a battery (assuming all the circuits are complete).

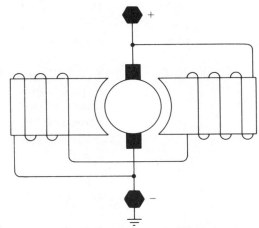

FIG. 7-5 Shunt-wound generator.

Residual magnetism

If you think about it, a self-exciting generator might at first seem to be an impossibility, because, when the cranking motor first starts to turn the engine over, and the generator pulley begins to rotate the armature, the armature produces no current to supply to the field. Without current, the field cannot produce lines of magnetic force. And without lines of magnetic force, the armature cannot produce current. The solution to this apparent contradiction is residual magnetism. The soft-iron, field pole shoes retain a certain amount of magnetism from previous operations, so a few lines of magnetic flux exist in the field assembly when the armature starts to rotate.

The lines of force from residual magnetism allow the armature to generate a small amount of current when it first starts to rotate. This current is fed back into the field coils, which create more lines of force, which allow more current to be generated. In short order, the generator has excited itself up to the regulated output.

1. *What does "shunt-wound" mean?*
2. *Where does a self-excited generator get the current for field operation?*
3. *What is responsible for the few lines of magnetic force that exist in the field windings when the armature first starts to turn over?*

Polarizing

You might ask now: How do the pole shoes acquire residual magnetism to begin with—before the generator is operated for the first time? The answer is to operate the generator as a motor. The positive post of the battery is connected to what will be the positive terminal of the generator. And the negative battery post is connected to what will be the negative terminal of the generator. The current flowing through the generator will create lines of force. These lines of force will be present whether the generator is allowed to rotate as a true motor, or if it is held stationary by the V-belt drive pulley.

The residual lines of magnetic force will circle through the field in a particular direction. This direction is called the *polarization* of the generator. The direction of polarization will determine which direction the current flows from the armature. Every new or rebuilt generator must be polarized so that it will have residual lines of magnetic force circling in the proper direction.

1. *How does the field acquire residual magnetism to being with— before it is used for the first time?*
2. *How does polarization affect the current coming from the armature?*

Cooling

As current flows through the field and as it is induced in the armature, heat builds up in the windings of both. In early-model generators, where voltage and current output was low, this was no problem. However, as electrical demands on the generator increased, it became necessary to remove some of the heat buildup. This is usually accomplished by a fan mounted behind the drive pulley on the outside of the generator (Fig. 7-6). The fan operates in a centrifugal manner, drawing cool air through the rear of the generator across the armature and field windings, then expelling the heated air off the tips of the fan blades.

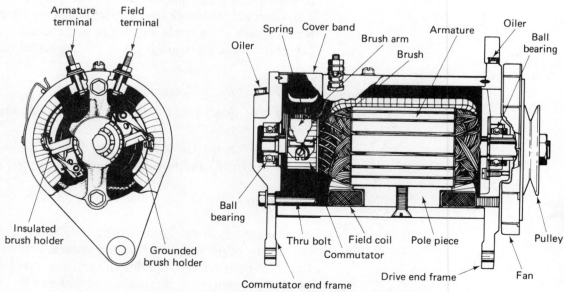

FIG. 7-6 Note the fan at the right end of this generator.

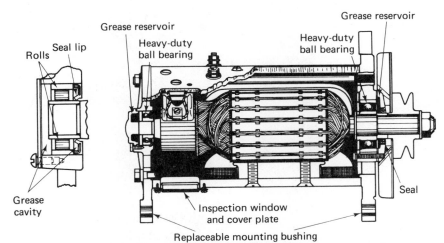

Grease reservoir

Heavy-duty ball bearing

Grease reservoir

Heavy-duty ball bearing

Seal lip

Rolls

Seal

Grease cavity

Inspection window and cover plate

Replaceable mounting bushing

FIG. 7-7 Note the permanent bearing lubrication features of this generator.

Lubrication

In early-model generators, the bearings at both ends were oiled from external filler cups. This arrangement required a regular maintenance schedule, which was usually not followed. And even when the generator was oiled, there was tendency among most operators to over-oil the rear bearings, which resulted in a heavy oil film coating on the commutator section. To avoid this problem, manufacturers began providing generators with sealed, prelubricated bearings (Fig. 7-7). These bearings require no regular service and last a long time.

1. *What is the usual method of removing heat buildup from the generator?*

2. *How were older-style generators lubricated?*

3. *What kind of bearings are used in newer generators?*

COMMUTATION— AC TO DC

In Chapter 4, the basic principle of induced electrical flow was introduced using a simple, single-loop armature for illustration. It was noted that current flow in each side of the loop changes direction as the sides move up and down. This output was called alternating current.

Figure 7-8 shows how ac current flow is typically diagrammed. The horizontal graph line represents degrees of armature rotation, with 360 degrees being one complete revolution. The vertical scale shows how much voltage is produced at different stages of armature rotation. The voltage above the horizontal line is responsible for flow in one direction; the voltage below the line provides current flow in the other direction.

When the armature first starts to rotate, at zero degrees rotation

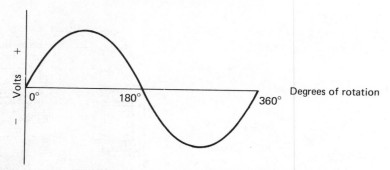

FIG. 7-8   Ac output from single-loop generator.

the voltage output is zero. Voltage builds up to a maximum above the horizontal line when the loop has rotated 90 degrees. After that, the voltage falls back down to zero when the loop has rotated 180 degrees.

At 180 degrees, the sides of the loop change direction. The side that was cutting *down* through the lines of force now goes *up*, and the side that was going *up* cuts *down* across the lines. Consequently, the current flow changes direction and the voltage curve moves below the horizontal line (assuming that the circuit remains complete, which is always necessary for current flow). The voltage reaches a maximum reverse level after 90 degrees (270 degrees total rotation) and returns to zero when the loop has gone through a complete revolution or 360 degrees. This is the starting point, where voltage builds back up again in the other direction.

Since this ac output cannot be used by the battery for charging, a split-ring commutator changes the ac to dc. Viewing the action of an armature loop as first pushing current in one direction, then pulling it in the other, the commutator allows the loop to push current along one-half of the circuit and pull it on the other half. As a result, current flows in the same direction in both halves.

Figure 7-9 diagrams dc current flow. As before, the voltage builds up to a maximum at 90 degrees, then returns to zero at 180 degrees. But this time, instead of reversing directions, it builds back up again on the same side of the horizontal line.

The current flow in this simple dc generator pulsates, going from zero to maximum voltage and then back to zero every 180 degrees of armature rotation. In actual practice such wide voltage fluc-

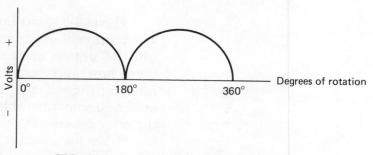

FIG. 7-9   Dc output from single-loop generator.

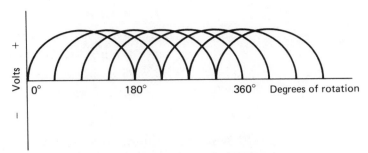

FIG. 7-10 Dc output from multiple-loop generator.

tions would be unacceptable. The solution is to use a number of armature loops, the ends of each loop attached to its own commutator segment. As the voltage from one loop begins to fall off, the voltage from the other loops builds up. The maximums and minimums blend together so that the average voltage at any given time is nearly constant. Figure 7-10 shows how this looks in a voltage diagram.

1. *At what periods (degrees) of armature rotation is the voltage output from the generator at zero?*
2. *At what degrees of armature rotation does the voltage build to a maximum—above and below the horizontal line?*
3. *What does a split-ring commutator do to the pushes and pulls from the armature?*
4. *At what degrees of armature rotation does the dc output from the commutator reach its maximum and minimum levels?*
5. *What is the solution to wide voltage fluctuations from a single-loop armature?*

ALTERNATORS

BASIC PRINCIPLES The basic operating principles of an alternator and a generator are the same. That is, relative motion between lines of flux and a conductor induces voltage, which, in turn, causes current flow in the conductor when the circuit is complete. The main differences between the alternator and the generator are the parts that rotate and the parts that remain stationary. In the generator the center armature rotates through the lines of force coming from the outside field. However, in the alternator, the conductor is stationary and the magnetic lines of force rotate. The effect is the same as in the generator. Induced current flows due to relative motion between the lines of force and the conductor.

In an alternator the outside conductor is called the *stator*, because it remains stationary. The center coil, where the lines of force are created, is called the *rotor*, for obvious reasons.

1. *What is necessary for induced current flow?*

2. *What moves in the generator and what remains stationary?*

3. *What is stationary in an alternator and what rotates?*

4. *In an alternator, what do you call the stationary part and what do you call the rotating part?*

REASONS FOR ALTERNATOR

Alternators are now virtually standard equipment on all cars produced throughout the world. One reason is the changing driving habits of the average motorist. In the past, most driving was on open roads, where the generator could operate at higher speeds and produce the required charging current more easily. However, with the increasing urbanization of life in most industrialized countries, people spend more and more time in stop-and-go driving. As a result, engines operate longer periods at idle speeds.

At these lower armature speeds, a typical dc generator has trouble producing sufficient current for large, accessory-laden automobiles. Even if the drive pulleys were changed so that the generator turned faster, the heavy loop-wound armature might become damaged due to centrifugal force at high engine speeds.

An alternator does not have these problems. The rotor is lighter and more stable. A typical alternator can rotate 30% faster than a generator, producing correspondingly more current.

1. *Why can't a generator's drive pulley be changed so that it will rotate faster and produce more current?*

2. *How much faster than a generator will an alternator rotate?*

CONSTRUCTION

The basic components of most alternators are the stationary stator, the rotating rotor, two end frames to support these components, a shaft, and a variety of diodes, and in some cases, transistors.

Stator

The stator contains three main sets of windings wrapped in slots around a laminated, circular iron frame (Fig. 7-11). A typical winding is made up of seven coils, which in turn are made up of a number of individual loops connected in series. The voltage produced in one loop is added to the next, and the voltage produced in one coil is added to the next.

Each main group of windings has two leads or ends, one lead where current enters the winding and one where current leaves. The leads are joined in two basic ways. In the so-called *Y connection* [Fig. 7-12(a)], one lead from each group of windings is joined in one common junction. The other leads branch out in a Y pattern from that single connection. In the *delta* or triangular connection [Fig. 7-12(b)], the lead at one end of a group of windings is joined to the

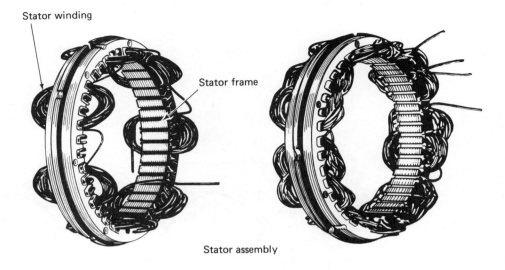

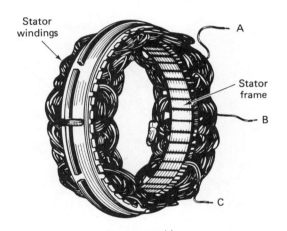

FIG. 7-11 Stator construction.

lead at the other end of the next group, which is joined to the lead at the end of the next group, and so on. The Y configuration is the most common.

Note: Those schematics should not be taken too literally. As the other illustrations show, the stator does not actually look the way it is pictured in the schematics. Schematics only show, in a very simple fashion, the "scheme" or logic of a connection, not the actual hardware.

There is, however, one bit of literal information that can be taken from the schematics. Notice that each main group of windings occupies one-third of the stator, or, considering the stator as a circle with 360 degrees, each group takes up 120 degrees of the circle. This means that the output from the stator is divided into three steps, or phases. As the rotor turns, first one phase will produce current, then

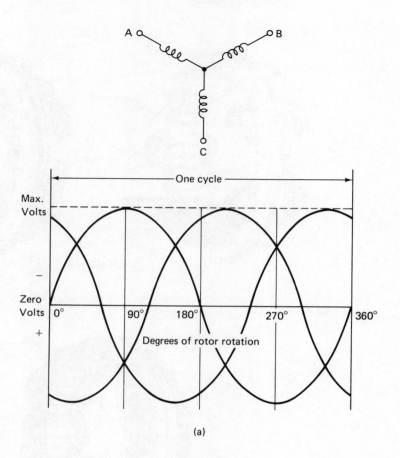

(a)

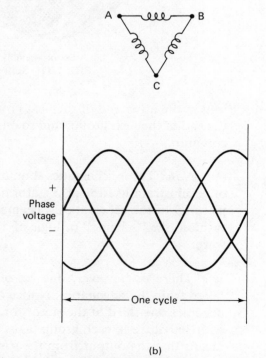

(b)

FIG. 7-12 (a) Y-connected stator. (b) Delta-connected stator.

the next, then the next. Alternators of this type are usually referred to as three-phase units.

1. *How many main sets of windings does the stator contain?*
2. *How many lead endings does each main winding have?*
3. *How are the lead endings connected in a Y connection?*
4. *In a three-phase alternator, is current produced from all the phases at the same time or from one phase, then another?*

Rotors

A typical rotor has four main components [Fig. 7-13(a)]. At the center is a drum-shaped coil of wire. Surrounding the coil are a pair of iron cups. The rims of the cups are formed into fingerlike projec-

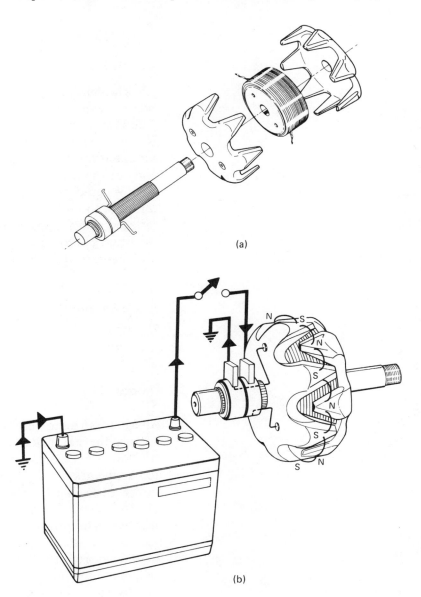

(a)

(b)

FIG. 7-13 (a) Rotor components. (b) Lines of force alternately magnetize fingers.

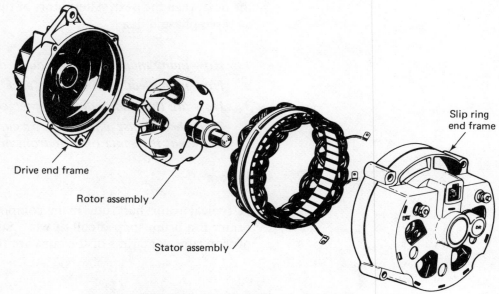

Drive end frame

Rotor assembly

Stator assembly

Slip ring end frame

FIG. 7-14 Stator and rotor components combined.

tions which interlace around the coil like the joined fingers of two hands. A shaft is passed through the center of both cups and the coil. The shaft is mounted on bearings at both ends. Current for the rotor is delivered by brushes riding against insulated copper slip rings mounted on the rotor shaft. The slip rings are connected to the two ends of the rotor coil.

When current passes through the rotor coil, a magnetic field is set up in the windings. The lines of force snake in and out of the interlaced iron fingers surrounding the coil [Fig. 7-13(b)]. As a result, the fingers become magnetized, one finger acquiring a north polarity, the next a south, and so on (Fig. 7-14).

1. *What are the main components of the rotor?*
2. *How do the lines of force coming from the coil move through the iron fingers surrounding the coil?*

Diodes

Alternators cannot use a split-ring commutator to change ac to dc because the stator does not rotate. So diodes of the kind introduced in Chapter 6 are employed to change or rectify the current from ac to dc. Acting as one-way valves, the diodes switch the current flow back and forth so that it flows out of the alternator in only one direction.

An alternator usually has six diodes, three positive and three negative. The positive diodes are mounted in a "heat sink" on the back of the alternator (Fig. 7-15). Heat from reverse bias voltage is conducted from the diodes to the metal heat sink and from there it is radiated to the surrounding air. The three negative diodes are attached directly to the end plate of the alternator. This provides a ground return circuit for the alternator output through these diodes.

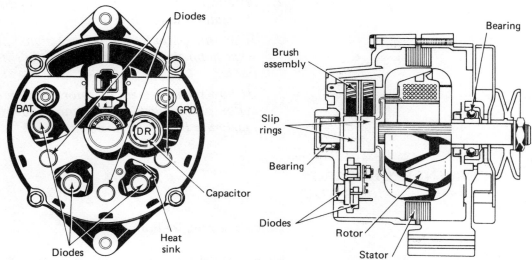

FIG. 7-15 Note diodes at rear of alternator.

1. *What kind of device is used to rectify alternator ac output to dc?*
2. *How many diodes does an alternator generally contain? How many of these are positive and how many negative?*
3. *Where are the positive diodes located, and why?*
4. *Where are the negative diodes located, and why?*

CURRENT FLOW (AC)   As the rotor poles turn within the stator, voltage is induced in the stator phases. Looking at a single stator phase, current flows in one direction for 180 degrees of rotor rotation, then in the other direction for the remaining 180 degrees of rotation as opposite polarity poles pass by. Assuming that a complete circuit exists, the voltage from any given phase reaches a peak above the horizontal line at 90° and 270 degrees. At these points the magnetic region cutting across the stator windings is strongest. The voltage drops to zero at zero, 180, and 360 degrees of rotor rotation, when the magnetism is weakest. Figure 7-16 diagrams the output from a three-phase unit.

FIG. 7-16 Comparison of (a) single-loop ac and (b) three-phase ac.

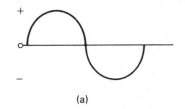

(a)

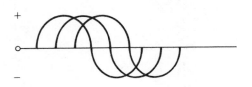

(b)

1. *After how many degrees of rotor rotation does the output from the stator change direction?*

2. *When the output from a given stator phase changes direction, what happens to the polarity of the rotor poles passing by the phase?*

3. *At how many degrees of rotor rotation does the output from a stator phase reach a maximum above the horizontal line? A maximum below the horizontal line?*

CURRENT RECTIFICATION
(AC TO DC)

Half-wave rectification

Figure 7-17 is a schematic representation of one phase connected to one diode. The phase is shown as a single strand coiled into several loops. The diode symbol is a solid arrowhead pointing to a short vertical line. The direction the diode will allow current to flow is noted by the adjacent (+) and (−) signs. The diode will allow current to flow when it is forward-biased, that is, when the current enters positive to (+) or negative to (−). Otherwise, it is reversed-biased and will not allow current to flow. The output from the phase windings is also noted by (+) and (−) signs. These signs switch positions when opposite poles of the rotor pass by the phase.

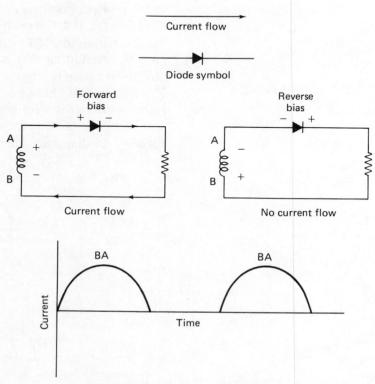

FIG. 7-17   Halfwave rectification.

For 180 degrees of rotor rotation, current will flow in a forward bias direction. It will pass through the diode and the attached circuit. For the other 180 degrees of rotor rotation, the current will be reversed-biased and will not pass through the diode or the attached circuit.

The current flow diagram in Fig. 7-17 shows that the single diode simply blocks out half the output from the phase. The entire lower wave is eliminated. Consequently, this is known as *half-wave rectification.*

1. *What happens to reverse current flow when a single diode is attached to the output circuit of an alternator phase?*
2. *What kind of rectification eliminates half an alternator phase's output?*

Full-wave rectification

Half-wave rectification is not desirable because too much of the alternator's output is eliminated. To solve this problem, engineers devised a system using the six diodes mentioned before. It is called *full-wave rectification.*

Figure 7-18 illustrates the full-wave rectifying system [Fig. 7-18(a)]. But before examining the flow paths, the parts will be noted. The diodes are known collectively as the *rectifier bridge* [Fig. 7-18(b)]. The three alternator phases are identified as A, B, and C. [Fig. 7-18(b)–(g)]. Because they are connceted in a Y pattern, one end of each phase is joined at the common center junction. The other ends are connected into the rectifier bridge. As the rotor turns, current is induced in successive phases. In each phase, current is induced first in one direction, then in the opposite direction.

Figure 7-18(b) shows the flow path in one direction from phase A. Electrons are pushed (1) out of the loop (2) through a forward bias diode (3) to ground (4) through the ground return circuit, (5) then to the negative pole of the battery. When alternator voltage (EMF) is greater than battery voltage (CEMF), electrons are pushed through the battery in a reverse direction for charging. The electrons then go to the battery terminal on the rectifier bridge. From there, the electrons pass through a forward bias diode, go into phase winding B, and return to phase winding A by way of the common connector Y junction. This completes the circuit.

The reverse output from phase A is shown in Fig. 7-18(c). In this case electrons are pushed from phase A through the Y junction into the windings of phase B. From there, the electrons go on to the rectifying bridge, to ground, through the battery in a reverse direction for charging, then back to the rectifying bridge to the end of phase A to complete the circuit.

The flow paths for the other two phases are shown in Fig. 7-18(d)–(g). Notice in each case that electrons are pushed from the phase windings, to the rectifying bridge, to ground, through the bat-

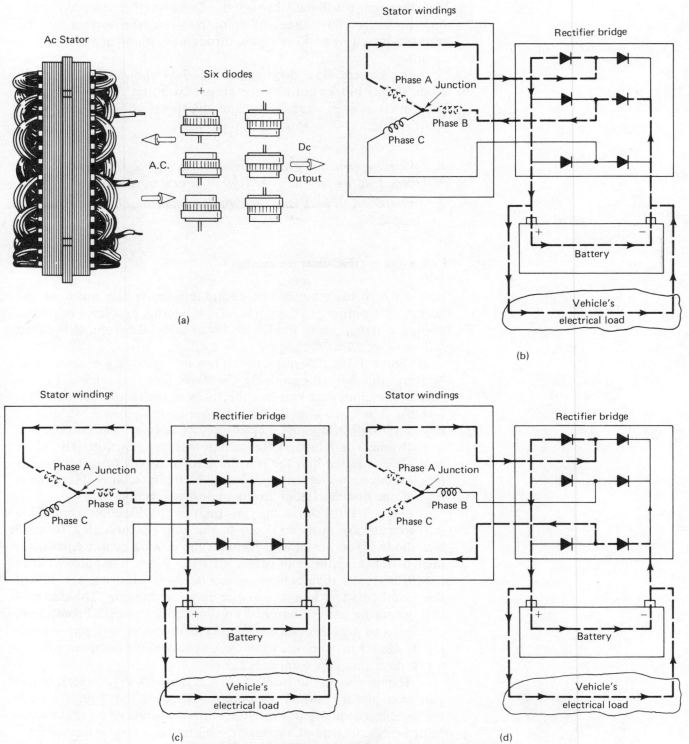

FIG. 7-18 (a) Full-wave rectification. (b)–(g) Diode-rectified three-phase output.

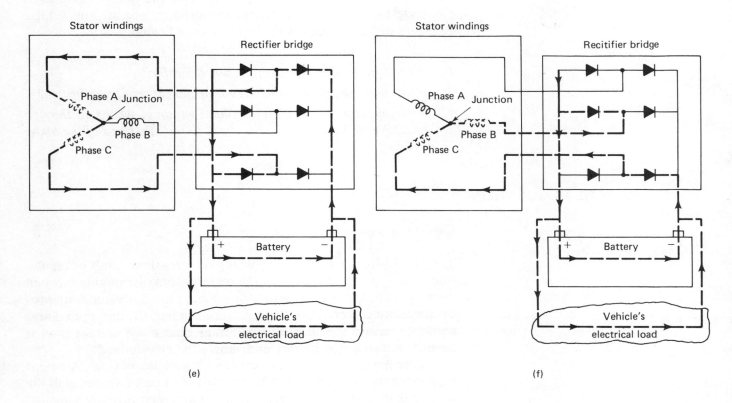

(e)   (f)

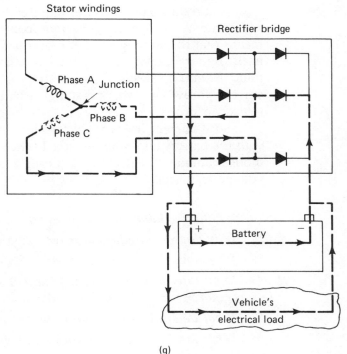

(g)

FIG. 7-18 (*continued*)

tery, then back to the rectifying bridge and the phase windings to complete the circuit. The current required to operate the vehicle branches off these circuits in the manner indicated.

1. *Why is half-wave rectification not desirable?*
2. *How many diodes are included in a typical rectifying bridge?*
3. *After electrons leave a stator phase winding, where do they go next? Next? Next? All the way back to the other end of the phase winding?*

VOLTAGE REGULATION

Generator versus alternator

The output from a generator typically requires three kinds of regulation. The cutout relay prevents the battery from discharging through the generator, the current regulator prevents the generator from producing more current than the armature can handle, and the voltage regulator causes the generator to produce no more voltage than is needed to charge the battery and satisfy the vehicle load.

Alternators do not require all these regulating devices. A cutout relay is not needed, because battery current cannot pass through the reverse bias diodes in the rectifier bridge to reach the alternator.

A current regulator is not required because the alternator is not self-excited. Its operating current comes from the battery. This means that the alternator cannot produce enough current to damage itself. Battery CEMF and the load in various operating circuits determine the current levels. At low battery CEMF or load the alternator current "draw" is high, and at higher battery CEMF or load the current draw drops.

So if current levels are determined by a push–pull relationship with the battery and other devices in the operating circuits and if the diodes eliminate the need for a cutout relay, the only control left is a voltage regulator.

1. *What three kinds of regulators does a generator typically require?*
2. *Why doesn't an alternator require a cutout relay?*
3. *Why doesn't an alternator require a current regulator?*
4. *Is an alternator self-excited, and if not, where does the rotor acquire current for operation?*
5. *What determines alternator current output?*
6. *What kind of regulator does an alternator require?*

Two kinds of voltage regulators

There are two basic kinds of voltage regulators used in alternators. Mechanical regulators are used in older-style alternators. Modern units use a transistorized system to regulate voltage.

Mechanical Voltage Regulators: The basic components in a mechanical regulating system are a set of spring loaded contact points, a nearby electromagnet coil, and a resistance element (Fig. 7-19). When the points are closed, current flows from the battery through the points to the alternator's rotor. Current also flows through the electromagnetic coil. As the battery is charged by the

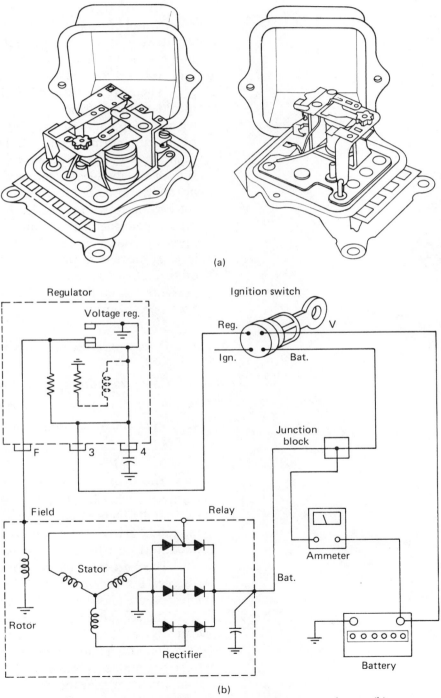

(a)

(b)

FIG. 7-19 (a) Double-contact-type generator regulators. (b) Single-unit regulator with ammeter.

alternator, the battery's voltage increases, strengthening the coil's attraction for the nearby, spring-loaded points. At a predetermined voltage level, the coil is able to overcome the spring tension and pull the points open. This cuts the circuit to the rotor. The voltage of the alternator drops, which allows the battery to discharge. As a result, the power of the coil is reduced, which allows spring tension to close the points and start the process over again (and again and again many times a second).

In most mechanical voltage-regulating systems, the power to the rotor is not cut completely. If it were, there would be a complete loss of flux and uneven power output. The resistor, which bypasses the points, allows a reduced, safe level of current to flow from the battery to the rotor while the points are open.

There are a variety of mechanical voltage regulating systems used in older-model vehicles, some with single contact points and some with dual points. In the single-point system described above, the points are normally closed. In the dual-point system, one of the points is normally open and one normally closed. The normally closed side of the dual-point set serves somewhat the same purpose as the normally closed points in a single-point regulator. It provides a path for current flow to maintain the operation of the alternator. The normally open side of the point set closes when the normally closed side opens. It routes current through a resistor circuit, allowing a reduced level of current to flow from the battery to the alternator while the other half of the point set is open. As in a single-point system, this prevents a complete loss of flux in the rotor, thereby maintaining an even power output.

1. *What are the basic components of a mechanical voltage regulator?*
2. *When the points are closed, where does current flow?*
3. *What causes the points to open?*
4. *What causes the points to close again?*
5. *What is the purpose of the resistor?*

Transistor Regulation: Transistorized voltage regulators perform somewhat better than mechanical systems. Transistorized units can handle higher current loads, and, because they contain no moving parts, are more reliable. Also, given the economics of mass production, transistorized systems can be less expensive.

There are three basic kinds of transistorized systems. One is called *discreet*, not because it can keep secrets but because many of its parts are separate and removable. Individual components can be replaced.

The second kind is called a *hybrid* unit. It represents a more recent "generation" of electronic development. It still has some separate, individual components. But most parts are encapsulated into self-contained groups. Only the groups may be replaced, not the components within the groups.

The most recent development in transistorized voltage regulators is the *monolithic* unit. It is produced by sophisticated electronic techniques so that the individual components are joined together into one unit. This kind of device is usually incorporated in the body of the alternator itself, whereas the other types of systems are separate from the alternator. And, unlike the other devices, the entire monolithic unit must be replaced if it fails. The individual components are not removable.

Figure 7-20 diagrams a simplified transistorized regulating system. It contains two transistors, one Zener diode, and four resistance elements. One of the resistance elements is heat-sensitive; another is adjustable. Because of the transistors and the diodes, the operation is best explained in terms of *hole* movement.

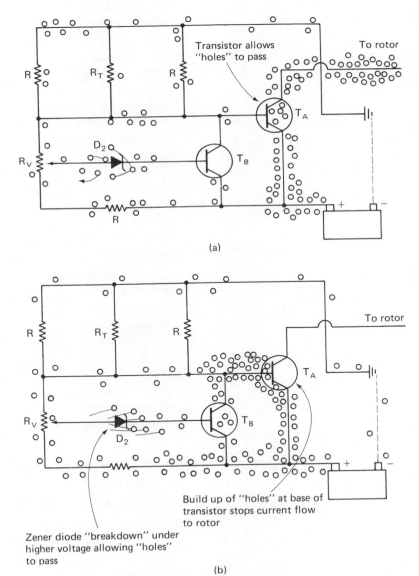

FIG. 7-20 Transistorized regulating system. (a) Voltage below maximum output. (b) Voltage above maximum output.

Positively charged holes come from the positive terminal of the battery. After entering the regulator, they immediately branch out into two paths. One branch leads to the emitter of transistor A. Most of these holes go directly into A's collector and back out of the regulator to the alternator's rotor. The rest of the holes that entered A's emitter go from the emitter into A's base circuit.

The current that doesn't enter the A branch goes to a second junction. Some of these hole's current goes to transistor B; some go into the resistor network. The base circuit for transistor B is connected to a variable resistor by the Zener diode. This diode is the main sensing element in the regulator. It is reverse-biased against hole movement from transistor B until the voltage reaches the breakdown level of the diode.

The Zener diode breakdown level corresponds to the maximum voltage output allowed for the alternator. When that level is reached, reverse-biased current passes through the Zener diode and transistor B is switched on. Current can now flow from the emitter to the collector of transistor B. This current goes into the resistor network as well as the base of transistor A. The current impressed on the base of transistor A has the same voltage impressed on the emitter. These two voltages act against each other, allowing no current to pass from the collector. The transistor is then switched off and no current goes to the rotor.

With the rotor and stator producing no current, the charging output of the battery falls off. This, in turn, affects the voltage pushing in a reverse direction against the Zener diode. In a fraction of a second, the voltage drops below the breakdown level, which allows transistor A to pass current again to the rotor. Then the charging voltage builds up and the process repeats itself.

The variable resistor Rv, is used to control the voltage output. The reverse-bias voltage passing through the Zener diode will be higher or lower, depending on where the diode is connected to the variable resistor.

The temperature-sensitive resistor also affects the voltage output. When the temperature is low, if offers more resistance to current flow, causing the Zener diode to breakdown at higher voltages. This allows the alternator to operate at higher voltage levels. Then, when the temperature goes up, the breakdown level goes down, which reduces the voltage output.

1. *Why are transistorized voltage regulators better than mechanical regulators?*

2. *What are the three basic kinds of transistorized systems?*

3. *When current is flowing to the rotor from the regulator, is transistor A switched on or off? What about transistor B?*

4. *What are the conditions of transistors A and B when no current is flowing to the rotor?*

5. *What is the main sensing element in the regulator?*

chapter

8

Points-type Ignition Systems

INTRODUCTION The basic purpose of the ignition system is to provide a spark to ignite the air/fuel mixture in the combustion chamber. The spark is produced at the tip of the spark plugs and it is timed to occur at just the proper instant for efficient combustion. Generally, the spark takes place while the piston is in the later part of the compression stroke: just before, just as, or just after the piston reaches TDC.

The basic parts of a conventional ignition system are the ignition distributor, spark plugs, coil, and associated wiring. The battery and ignition switch are also considered part of the ignition system. This chapter details the operation of a "point-type" ignition system. Chapter 9 covers electronic ignitions.

PRIMARY AND SECONDARY CIRCUITS Although the battery is considered part of the ignition system, normal battery current (12 V or 6 V) does not have enough electrical pressure or voltage to force electrons across the spark plug's air gap. It cannot create the spark needed to ignite the air/fuel mixture. To obtain the proper spark, the battery voltage must be stepped up by the coil to as much as 30,000 V (see Fig. 8-1).

The parts of the ignition system that carry the higher voltage

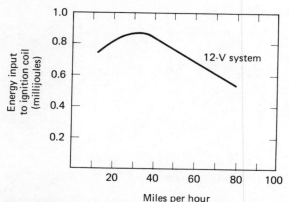

FIG. 8-1 Relationship between engine speed and input to ignition coil.

produced by the coil are called the *secondary circuit* (Fig. 8-2). Included in the secondary circuit are the spark plugs, spark plug cables, distributor rotor button, distributor cap, and secondary windings inside the coil.

The parts of the ignition system that carry lower voltage, battery current are called the *primary circuit* (Fig. 8-2). They include the ignition switch, distributor points, condenser, and the primary windings in the coil. The battery is also considered part of the primary circuit.

In view of this, the function of the ignition system can be more specifically defined as converting lower-voltage, battery current into the higher voltage needed to produce a sufficient spark at the spark plug's gap *and* delivering this high-voltage surge to the proper spark plug at the proper time.

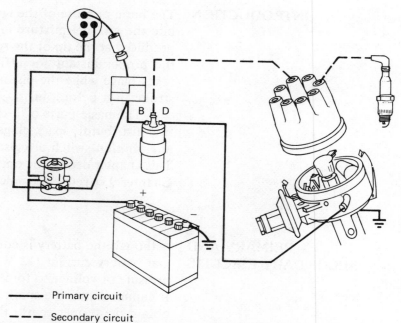

———— Primary circuit

– – – – Secondary circuit

FIG. 8-2 Primary and secondary ignition system circuits.

1. *Are 6 or 12 volts enough to create an adequate spark at the spark plug?*
2. *What elements in the ignition system step up battery voltage?*
3. *What do you call the circuit that carries the higher voltage?*
4. *What do you call the circuit that carries the lower voltage?*
5. *What elements are included in the primary circuit?*
6. *What elements are included in the secondary circuit?*

CURRENT FLOW IN THE IGNITION SYSTEM

Before going into the operation and function of the various components in the ignition system, the flow of current through the primary and secondary circuits of a "points-type" ignition system will be traced.

Primary circuit up to the coil . . .

Looking first at the primary circuit, electrical flow begins at the battery's positive terminal. From there it goes to the ignition switch. The ignition switch is the central junction station for almost the entire electrical system. Current must flow through it whenever any system is in operation.

After passing through the ignition switch, current flows to the ignition coil. The current follows one of two paths to the coil, depending on the position of the ignition switch.

If the switch is in the "run" position, the current flows through a calibrated resistance wire (or other resistance element); see Fig. 8-3. This resistance element reduces the amount of voltage delivered to the ignition system during normal running and helps protect the ignition components (particularly the points) from excessive voltage.

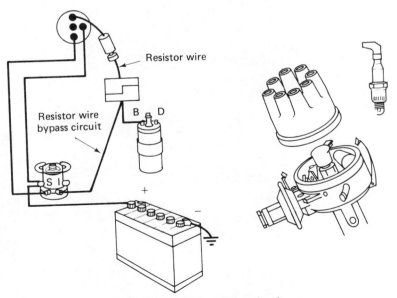

FIG. 8-3 Bypass resistor circuit.

When the ignition switch is in the "start" position, the resistance is bypassed. During starting, the ignition system needs full battery voltage to overcome the starting loads.

1.   Where does current flow begin in the primary circuit?

2.   Where does the current go from there?

3.   How many paths can the current follow from the ignition switch to the coil?

4.   What path does the current follow when the switch is in the "run" position?

5.   What is the function of the calibrated resistance wire?

6.   What path does the current follow when the switch is in the "start" position?

Current flow in the coil . . .

The coil, the next destination of the current, is composed of a number of wires wound (appropriately enough) in the form of a coil. There are two separate sets of these windings, one inside the other, as noted in Fig. 8-4.

The outside set of windings is called the *primary side* of the coil. It is part of the ignition system's primary circuit and handles only battery voltage. Primary current enters the coil at the one end of the primary windings and comes out at the other end.

The inner windings are called the *secondary side* of the coil and are part of the secondary circuit. The high-voltage surge needed to fire the spark plugs is created in the secondary windings.

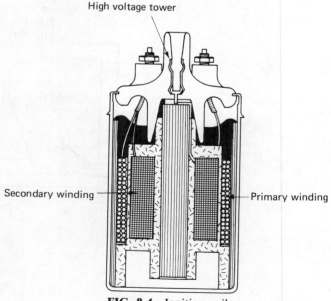

FIG. 8-4   Ignition coil.

1. *How many sets of windings are in the coil, and how are they located with respect to one another?*
2. *What is the outside set of windings called?*
3. *What kind of voltage does it handle?*
4. *What is the inside set of windings called?*
5. *What happens in the inside set of windings?*

Primary current flow in the distributor . . .

Lower voltage, primary current flows through the primary side of the coil to the points inside the distributor. The points are a simple electrical switch that can interrupt the flow of current in the ignition's primary circuit (Fig. 8-5). One side of the switch (or one point) is mounted on a moving arm and the other point is mounted on the distributor plate. The points are brought into contact or moved apart by the action of the moving arm.

When the points are in contact, primary current flows between them and is returned by the grounded stationary point back through the engine ground to the battery. In this way a complete primary circuit is created. However, when the points are open or separated, there is no longer a complete path for current to flow through the ignition's primary circuit.

1. *Where does current go after leaving the coil?*
2. *Where are the points?*
3. *What function do they perform?*
4. *How are the points moved apart or brought into contact?*
5. *What happens when the points are in contact?*
6. *What happens when they are open?*

Flow of electricity in the secondary circuit . . .

When the points open, current stops flowing in the coil's primary windings. When that happens, a burst of high-voltage current originates in the secondary windings. This current goes from the coil to

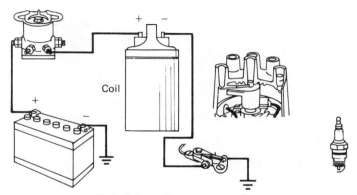

Coil

FIG. 8-5 Primary current flow.

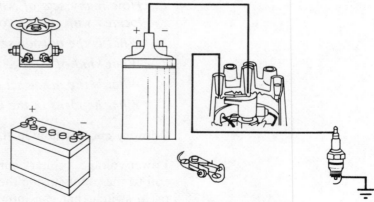

FIG. 8-6 Secondary current flow.

the distributor cap, to the distributor rotor, and then to the spark plugs (Fig. 8-6).

The following steps describe the path taken by the secondary current:

1. Current flows from the coil's secondary windings to the coil's high-tension cable.
2. Then the current flows along the high-tension cable to the center terminal on the distributor cap.
3. From the distributor's center terminal the current flows to the metal strip on the distributor rotor button.
4. The current flows along the metal strip to one of the distributor spark plug terminals (where the current leaps across the gap between the rotor tip and the terminal).
5. From there the current flows to the spark plug cable.
6. The current flows along the spark plug cable to the spark plug's center electrode.
7. The current arcs across the spark plug gap to the spark plug's side (or ground) electrode.
8. From the spark plug's side electrode the current flows to ground via the engine block.
9. The current flows through ground (engine block, frame, etc.) back to the battery's negative terminal.

1. What causes current to stop flowing in the coil's primary windings?

2. What causes the sudden burst of high-voltage current from the coil's secondary windings?

OPERATION OF THE COIL As you learned in Chapter 4, whenever current flows through a wire, a magnetic field is created around the wire. So, when the ignition points close, a magnetic field builds up around each turn of wire in the coil's primary windings, combining to build up a magnetic field around the entire primary side of the coil.

When the points open, current stops flowing through the primary windings. With no current flow, the magnetic field cannot be sustained. However, the field does not simply disappear. Instead, it tends to fall inward toward the center of the coil. The magnetic lines of force that were created by the primary windings cut across the thousands of turns of fine wire that make up the coil's secondary windings. As a result, the electron balance in the wire is upset and voltage is produced in the coil's secondary windings.

The current flow from the secondary windings has high voltage because the secondary windings are made up of many thousands of turns or loops of fine wire. As the magnetic field falls inward, it cuts across each turn of wire, generating a certain amount of pressure in every loop. Since the loops are connected in series, the voltage produced in one loop is added to the voltage produced in the succeeding loops. By the time the lines of force have fallen all the way to the center of the coil, the pressure totals 20,000 to 30,000 V.

In effect, the coil is a step-up transformer. Figure 8-7 illustrates the operation of a typical coil.

1. What builds up around each turn of wire on the primary side of the coil when the points are closed?

2. What happens to the magnetic field when the points open?

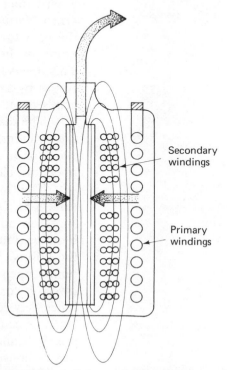

FIG. 8-7 Collapsing links or force induce voltage in secondary coils.

3. *What do the magnetic lines of force do to windings in the secondary?*
4. *What kind of wires make up the secondary windings?*
5. *What is produced in the coil's secondary side when the points are open and the lines of force cut across the secondary windings?*
6. *How much total voltage is built up in a typical secondary?*

OPERATION OF THE DISTRIBUTOR (PRIMARY SIDE)

The distributor has two main jobs. One is to interrupt the current flow in the primary circuit and thereby trigger the high-voltage surge from the coil's secondary. The other job is to deliver the secondary voltage to the proper spark plug at the proper time. You might say, its job is to trigger and conduct at the same time.

The first job is accomplished by the points, in a points-type distributor. One point is mounted on an insulated moving arm and the other is more or less stationary and grounded to the distributor base. When the points are open or moved apart, the current flow in the primary circuit is interrupted. When the points are closed, the flow continues.

The points are opened and closed by the action of the distributor breaker cam. The cam is located in the center of the distributor and is connected by the distributor drive shaft to the camshaft in the engine block. A spiral gear drive between the two shafts causes the distributor cam to turn at one-half the crankshaft speed.

The distributor cam has lobes or high places which push against a hard-fiber or nylon rubbing block on the point's moving arm. The arm is spring-loaded, so the rubbing block rides against the cam as the cam turns. When the cam lobe strikes the rubbing block, the point on the moving arm is pushed away from the stationary point. This opens the points. The points are closed when the rubbing block passes by the cam lobe, allowing spring tension to pull the moving arm's point back into contact with the stationary point.

The distributor breaker cam usually has as many lobes as there are cylinders in the engine, four lobes for a four-cylinder engine, eight for an eight, and so on. One complete revolution of the cam will open and close the points once for each cylinder in the engine.

The time when the points are closed is called the *dwell period*. (Fig. 8-8). Dwell can be considered the distance between two certain spots on adjacent cam lobes. The first spot is where the rubbing block is pulled far enough inward after passing a cam lobe to close the points. The second spot is where the next cam lobe pushes the points open again. The space between thse two spots is called the *dwell*. It corresponds to the time that the points are closed. The distance between the spots is measured in degrees, like degrees in a circle. The center of the distributor can be considered as the center of the circle and the arc (or circular distance) from one spot to the other can be considered as part of the circle's circumference.

The point closing or dwell period is important to the operation of the ignition system because the coil does not build up its magnetic

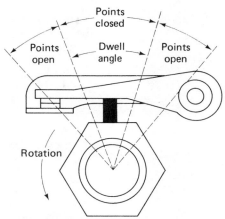

FIG. 8-8 Dwell is that portion of can rotation when the contacts are closed.

field instantly when current passes through the primary windings. Even moving at the speed of light it takes a certain amount of time for the current impulse to flow through the primary side of the coil. Therefore, the dwell period must be long enough to allow the coil to become fully energized before the points open again.

The dwell period, which is specified by the manufacturer, is adjustable, generally by changing the distance or gap between the points (Fig. 8-9). Usually, the gap is adjusted by loosening the hold-down screw(s) of the otherwise stationary plate-mounted point and then moving it in or away from the point on the moving arm. In some cases, the point gap is adjusted by turning a hex screw that is accessible through a "window" in the distributor case.

The opening between the points determines when the rubbing block will strike the cam lobes. This, in turn, affects the dwell period.

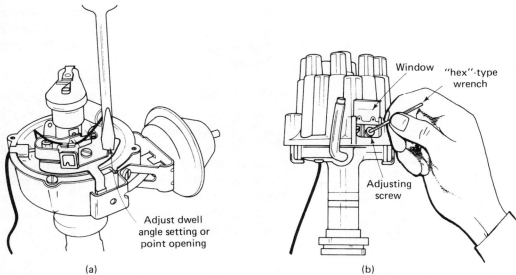

FIG. 8-9 (a) Using a screwdriver to adjust dwell. (b) Adjustment of dwell angle on external adjustment-type distributor.

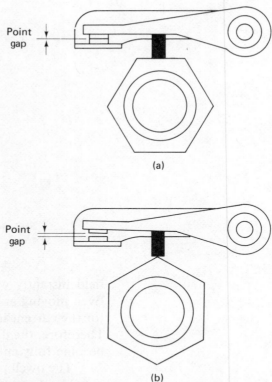

FIG. 8-10 (a) Point gap so close that dwell equals 360 °.
(b) Point gaped wide so that dwell equals 0 °.

For instance, in the extreme case shown in Fig. 8-10(a), the plate-mounted point is moved so close to the moving-arm point that it pushes the rubbing arm out of reach of the cam lobes. Because the cam lobes cannot strike the rubbing arm, the points in this example will never open and the dwell will be 360 degrees.

Going to the other extreme [Fig. 8-10(b)], if the stationary point is moved so far from the moving arm point that the rubbing block contacts the cam all the way around during the entire period of cam rotation, the points would never close and the dwell would be zero degrees.

Therefore, when the points are brought closer together, the rubbing block strikes the cam lobes later and the dwell is correspondingly increased. When the points are separated, the rubbing block is free to strike the cam lobes earlier and the dwell is decreased.

However, even though dwell and point gap are related, they are usually treated separately in an ignition system tune-up (Fig. 8-11). First, the point gap may be approximated by placing a feeler gauge between the points. Then, the dwell period (or dwell angle, as it is called) is measured electrically and more exactly by a dwell meter, which is attached to the distributor's, or coil's primary terminal and to ground.

Although dwell and point gap are often adjusted to manufacturers' specifications in the same way (by changing the distance between the points), the dwell meter is considered a much more ac-

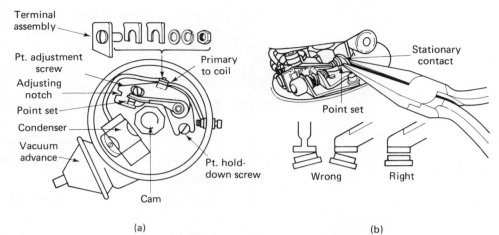

FIG. 8-11   (a) Inside the distributor. (b) Adjusting point alignment.

curate tool (Fig. 8-12). Its use, particularly in sensitive later-model engines, is recommended.

1. *What are the two jobs of the distributor?*
2. *Once again, what happens to primary flow when the points are open?*
3. *What happens to the primary flow when the points are closed?*
4. *Where is the distributor cam located?*
5. *What do you call the high places on the cam?*
6. *What do the high places push against?*
7. *Where is the rubbing block located?*
8. *How are the points opened?*
9. *How are they closed?*
10. *How many lobes does the breaker cam usually have?*
11. *What do you call the period when the points are closed?*
12. *What is dwell?*

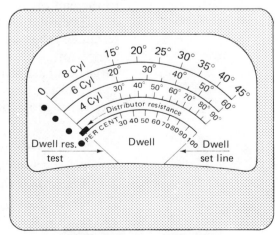

FIG. 8-12   Sun dwell meter.

13. *How is dwell measured?*

14. *How are the loops on the primary side of the coil energized—all at once or one at a time?*

15. *What do the lines of force from the outside loops do to the inside loops?*

16. *In which direction does the current induced by the outside loops flow?*

17. *What overcomes this current flow?*

18. *How long must the dwell period be?*

19. *How is dwell adjusted?*

20. *What happens to the dwell period when the points are brought closer together?*

21. *What happens to the dwell period when the points are separated?*

22. *How is point gap measured?*

23. *How is dwell angle measured?*

24. *Which is more accurate, a feeler gauge or a dwell meter?*

OPERATION OF THE DISTRIBUTOR (SECONDARY SIDE)

Delivering the high-voltage secondary surge to the correct spark plug cable at the proper time is the function of the distributor rotor button and distributor cap.

The cap [Fig. 8-13(a)] has a center terminal where the high-voltage surge enters the distributor. The surges leave the distributor at the distributor's spark plug terminals. The terminals are connected to the spark plug cables in the same sequence as the engine's firing order.

The current is routed from the center terminal to the distributor's spark plug terminals by the rotor button. The rotor button is attached to the top of the distributor cam and rotates with it. In this way, the button (1) picks up current from the center electrode at the button's metal strip, (2) routes the current to the end of the strip, and (3) delivers the current to the distributor spark plug terminal adjacent to the end of the strip [Fig. 8-13(b)].

The rotation of the button, the connections at the spark plug terminals, the opening of the points, and the distributor position of the piston in the cylinder are all arranged so that the high-voltage surge occurs at just the proper instant and at the proper cylinder. The spark must appear at the tip of the spark plug just as the air/fuel mixture is properly compressed for efficient combustion.

1. *What elements are responsible for delivering current to the correct spark plug at the proper time?*

2. *Where does the high-voltage surge enter the distributor?*

3. *Where does it leave the distributor?*

4. *What part of the distributor routes the high-voltage surge from one place to another?*

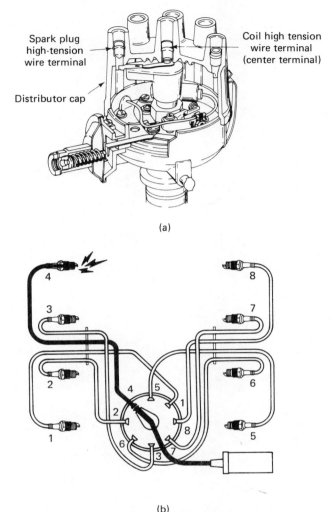

(a)

(b)

FIG. 8-13 Distributor primary components.

TIMING ADVANCE At an idle speed, the spark is timed to occur just before, just as, or just after the piston is at TDC in the compression stroke. However, as the engine speed increases, the spark must be advanced. That is, it must be made to occur earlier in the stroke. The time required to burn a given amount of the fuel remains much the same, regardless of the engine speed. However, at faster engine speeds there is less time available, so the burning process must be started sooner (Fig. 8-14).

The burning process must also be started earlier when the carburetor is at part throttle. At that time there will be a partial vacuum in the intake manifold and cylinders. Because of the partial vacuum, less fuel will be drawn from the carburetor to the cylinders during the intake stroke. The reduced amount of air/fuel mixture will not be compressed as much in the compression stroke as a full mixture. When the air/fuel mixture is less dense, it burns slower. So the burning process must be started sooner.

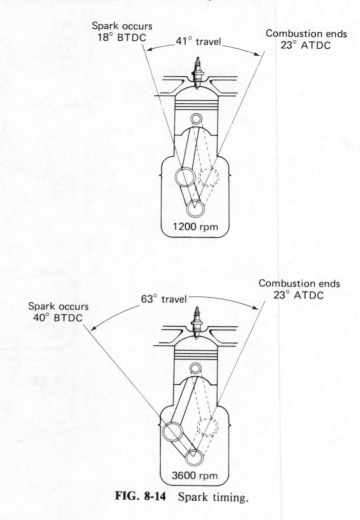

FIG. 8-14   Spark timing.

There are two principal ways of causing the burning process to begin earlier: the centrifugal advance and vacuum advance methods. The centrifugal advance is generally responsive to engine speed and the vacuum advance to carburetor conditions.

1.   *When is the spark timed to occur at idle speed?*

2.   *What must happen to the timing as engine speed increases?*

3.   *Does the engine speed have any effect on the time it takes to burn the air/fuel mixture?*

4.   *When must the burning process be started as the engine speed increases?*

5.   *What must happen to the timing when the carburetor is at part throttle?*

6.   *What is the condition in the intake manifold and cylinders when the carburetor is at part throttle?*

7.   *Will more or less air/fuel mixture be drawn into the cylinders when the carburetor is at part throttle?*

8.   *Will the mixture be compressed as much?*

9. *Will the burning process be longer or shorter?*

10. *What are two principal ways of causing the burning process to start sooner?*

Centrifugal (or mechanical) advance

In the centrifugal or mechanical advance systems, the timing is advanced by changing the position of the distributor cam. The cam is attached to the end of the distributor shaft in such a way that the cam can be rotated a certain amount independently of the shaft's rotation. When rotated in the proper direction, the cam lobes will strike the points' rubbing block earlier and thereby cause the points to open earlier. The faster the engine runs, the greater the advance will be.

The cam position is rotated or advanced by the action of two spring-loaded, calibrated weights. On some GM products, the weights are located under the rotor button. On most other cars, they are found beneath the breaker plate. The weights are attached directly to the distributor drive shaft and indirectly to the breaker cam.

As the engine speed increases, the centrifugal force acting against calibrated weights causes the weights to push against their springs and away from the rotating shaft. This action via the indirect connection with the distributor cam advances the position of the cam relative to the distributor shaft and causes the points to open earlier. The degrees of advance depends on the r/min of the shaft and the calibrated spring tension on the weights. On some model cars it can be as much as 45 degrees.

Figure 8-15 shows a GM-type centrifugal advance mechanism, and Fig. 8-16 the type of centrifugal advance used on most other cars.

1. *What is the nature of the connection between the distributor cam and the end of the distributor shaft?*

2. *What happens when the distributor cam is rotated in the proper direction with respect to the distributor shaft?*

3. *How is the cam's position advanced or rotated?*

4. *What force acts on the weights as the engine speed increases?*

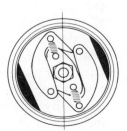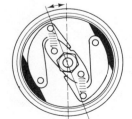

No advance   Full advance

FIG. 8-15 GM centrifugal advance.

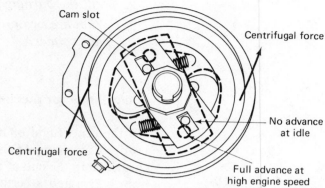

FIG. 8-16 Centrifugal spark advance used on other engines.

Vacuum method

Mechanical or centrifugal advance systems move the breaker cam to advance the spark. Vacuum systems move the distributor plate.

The breaker plate is a movable platform on which the points are mounted inside the distributor. The cam comes up through a hole in the center of the plate. The plate is movable so that it can be rotated around the cam.

When the plate is rotated, it changes the position of the moving arm's rubbing block with respect to the cam lobes. Depending on the position of the plate, the rubbing block will engage the lobes earlier or later. This, in turn, affects the times that the points open and close, which affects the times that the spark plugs fire.

In most vacuum systems, an air-pressure-sensitive diaphragm is used to change the position of the distributor plate. The diaphragm is located on the side of the distributor and is connected by an air line to the carburetor. The diaphragm and its linkages are arranged in such a way to move the distributor plate into an advanced position whenever there is a vacuum in the line from the carburetor.

The air line to the carburetor is connected just above the carburetor throttle plates when the plates are in the idle position, as shown in Fig. 8-17. At idle speed, the air line registers the atmospheric pressure above the throttle plates. At this time there is no movement of the distributor plate, and consequently no spark advance.

However, as the engine speeds up, the throttle begins to swing open and exposes the air line to the partial vacuum created in the cylinders. This causes the distributor plate to move into an advanced position. Then, as the throttle moves to a fully open position, the vacuum in the cylinders (and hence the air line) is reduced. The distributor plate is then returned back toward the basic timing setting by spring action.

Many engines have both centrifugal and vacuum advance mechanisms. At any given engine speed or throttle setting, one or both systems might be in operation. See Fig. 8-18 for the operation of a typical vacuum advance system.

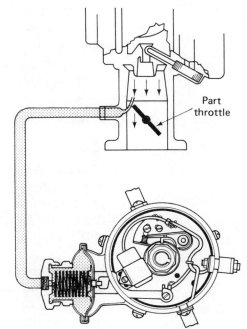

FIG. 8-17　Vacuum advance.

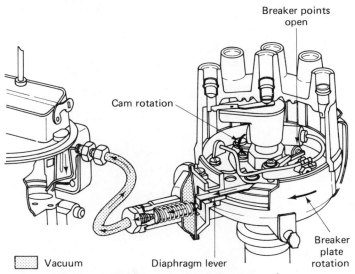

FIG. 8-18　Vacuum spark advance operation.

1.　*What moves in the vacuum advance system?*

2.　*What does the plate do when it rotates?*

3.　*What is used in most vacuum advance systems to advance the spark?*

4.　*The diaphragm is connected to something by an air line. What is that?*

5.　*How are the diaphragm and its linkage arranged?*

6.　*Does the distributor plate move when the throttle plate is in an idle position?*

7.   *What is the position of the throttle plate when the distributor plate begins to move?*

8.   *Does the distributor plate move back or advance when the throttle plate is in the fully open position?*

Basic timing

In any sort of timing advance system, there must be a starting point. This is called the *basic timing setting*. It is the position of the distributor plate and cam at idle speed when none of the advance systems are in operation. In older engines the basic timing is usually 5 to 10 degrees before TDC. Newer, pollution-control engines often operate at 0 ° TDC or as much as 4 ° ATDC.

Timing advance is usually fixed, unless the mechanism breaks. However, basic timing is adjustable according to manufacturers' specifications. Basic timing is usually adjusted by loosening the distributor lock-down bolt(s) and moving the distributor housing clockwise or counterclockwise [Fig. 8-19(a)]. The correctness of the adjustment can be determined by shining a timing light on markings inscribed on one of the crankshaft pulleys or on a plate alongside the pulley [Fig. 8-19(b)].

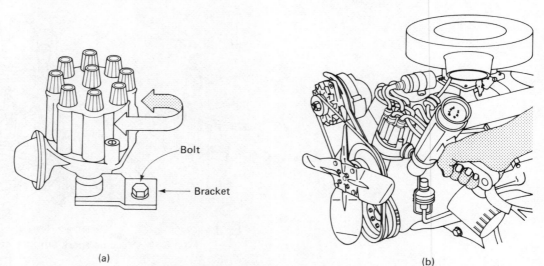

(a)   (b)

FIG. 8-19   (a) Moving distributor to change timing. (b) Aiming the timing light.

1.   *What do you call the position of the distributor plate and the breaker cam when none of the advance sytems are in operation?*

2.   *What is a common basic timing setting for older engines?*

3.   *What is a possible basic timing setting for newer engines?*

4.   *How is correctness of the basic timing setting determined?*

OPERATION OF THE CONDENSER

The condenser's job is to protect the points just as they start to open at the beginning of each firing cycle. This is what happens:

When the points open, the magnetic field around the coil's primary windings begins to collapse toward the center of the coil. The cutting action of the magnetic lines of force induces voltage or electrical pressure, which results in current flow in the coil's secondary windings. However, the collapsing lines of force also cut across the primary windings. So a certain amount of voltage is also generated there. If the resultant pressure causes current to flow to the partially open points, it will arc across the gap (Fig. 8-20). The points will become pitted as a result of the arcing and will shortly wear out.

Note: Although current cannot flow in an open circuit, when voltage is great enough, current can arc over small gaps, as in the case of the just-opened points.

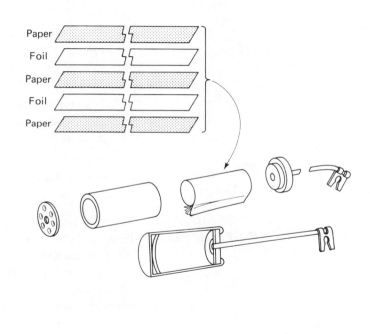

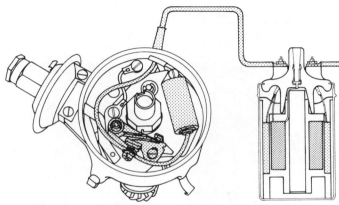

FIG. 8-20 Condenser.

The *condenser* (or capacitor, as it is called sometimes) provides an alternative path for current generated in the primary. The condenser includes two relatively wide, but thin metal plates. When the points open, current from the primary side of the coil flows to one of these plates. (The condenser is attached in a somewhat parallel manner to the points circuit and it is easier for current to go to the condenser than to attempt to jump the just-opened point gap.) In a short period of time, the current builds up a number of electrons on the thin metal plates. When the buildup becomes great enough, the condenser discharges back into the primary circuit. However, by that time, the points are full open and the charge cannot arc between the points and do any damage.

1. *What is the basic job of the condenser?*

2. *When the primary field collapses, where is current generated, besides in the secondary windings?*

3. *What will the current do if it is allowed to flow to the partially open points?*

4. *Where does the current generated in the primary side of the coil flow when the points are just barely opened?*

5. *What is the nature of the electrical connection between the condenser and the points circuit? In other words, is it series or parallel?*

6. *What is the condition of the points by the time the condenser discharges the electrons produced in the coil's primary windings?*

OPERATION OF THE SPARK PLUG

The spark plug is the focal point of the entire ignition system. It is here that the basic job of the ignition system takes place: igniting the air–fuel mixture.

A typical spark plug, as pictured in Fig. 8-21, has these basic components: (1) the terminal, (2) center electrode, (3) side electrode, (4) metal shell, and (5) insulator.

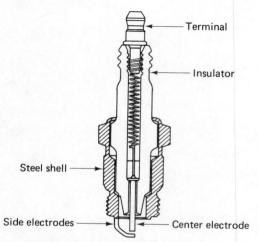

FIG. 8-21   Standard spark plug.

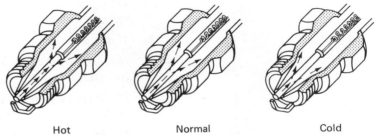

| Hot | Normal | Cold |

FIG. 8-22 Spark plug heat range.

Current enters the spark plug at the center terminal. Then it proceeds down the middle of the spark plug to the center electrode at the other end. If the electrical pressure is great enough, the current flow will jump across the air gap to the side electrode. The spark created at the gap ignites the air–fuel mixture. After that, the current proceeds to the metal shell to which the side electrode is fastened. The threaded metal shell is screwed into the engine block and provides a return ground path for the current flow.

The porcelain insulator, whose lower half is covered by the metal shell, has two basic functions. First, it is an electrical insulator that prevents short-circuiting between the center electrode and the metal shell. Second, its shape and design affect the heat-dissipation qualities of the spark plug, or *heat range*, as it is called.

The longer it takes heat to leave the tip of the spark plug (which projects into the hot combustion chamber), the hotter the spark plug will operate. Figure 8-22 shows the heat paths taken by spark plugs of several heat ranges. The heat flows through the insulator to the metal shell and from there to the engine block to be dissipated into the engine coolant.

The heat range of spark plugs is important because spark plugs are designed to operate at particular engine temperatures. If the engine is too hot for a particular spark plug, the electrodes may melt and the insulation become blistered and chipped. In these cases (not counting any other possible problems) a colder spark plug should be used. It has a shorter heat flow path, so it will dissipate heat quicker and operate cooler.

However, if the engine is too cold for the spark plugs being used, they may become fouled and sooty. In this instance (again, not counting any other problems) a hotter spark plug would be in order. Its heat-dissipation path is longer, so it does not throw off heat as quickly and operates hotter to burn off the sooty deposits.

Besides the functions noted in the preceding, many spark plugs also have a built-in antistatic device. It is called a *resistor* and it is placed in series inside the spark plug, between the terminal and the center electrode. The resistor's job is to reduce radio and TV interference from the ignition system. It also helps prevent electrode wear.

1.   What are the basic components of a typical spark plug?

2.   Where does current enter the spark plug?

3.   *What part of the spark plug contacts the engine block and provides a ground return path for the current flow?*

4.   *What are the two functions of the porcelain insulator?*

5.   *If a spark plug has a relatively long heat path, will its heat range be relatively hot or cold?*

6.   *If the spark plug in an engine is blistered and chipped, would you replace it with a plug whose heat range is colder or hotter?*

7.   *What kind of replacement spark plug would you use if the old plug was fouled and sooty?*

8.   *What is the resistor's job?*

chapter

9

Solid-State
Ignition Systems

INTRODUCTION As of 1977, all American-made automobiles were using solid-state ignition systems. Points-type systems had been eliminated entirely. It is not that points-type systems don't work well; they just don't work well enough in the present era of pollution controls and fuel scarcity. Solid-state systems provide higher voltages at the spark plugs and are able to control these voltages better. They also require less maintenance and are less likely to produce fuel-wasting, polluting misfires.

CONTACT-CONTROLLED TRANSISTORIZED SYSTEMS There are a number of devices that come under the general heading of solid-state or transistorized ignition systems. All are similar to points-type systems in these respects: all use ignition coils to create the high-voltage surge needed to operate the spark plugs and all use more-or-less standard secondary circuit components (rotor button, distributor cap, spark plug wires, etc.) to distribute this high voltage (Fig. 9-1). They differ from points-type ignitions basically in the way the primary circuit to the coil is interrupted to produce the high-voltage surge in the secondary.

The first solid-state or transistorized ignition systems were introduced in the late 1950s as optional or add-on equipment for other-

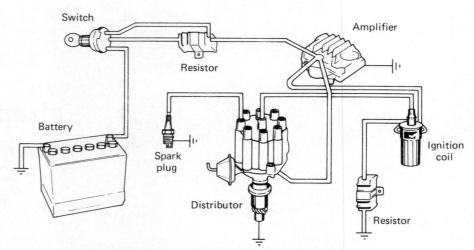

FIG. 9-1 Some components in contact-controlled transistorized ignition system.

wise conventional ignition systems. The main difference between conventional ignitions of that period and transistorized units was the primary circuit between the points and the ignition coil. In a standard, points-type ignition, current flows more or less directly from the ignition switch, through a resistor element (when the switch is in the "run" position), through the closed points to the primary windings in the ignition coil. When the points open, the flow is interrupted and a high-voltage surge is induced in the secondary windings of the coil.

Primary current flow in a contact-controlled transistorized system does not go directly from the points to the coil. Instead, it goes to the base circuit of a transistor in the amplifier module (see Fig. 9-2). The base circuit of a transistor (as you learned in Chapter 6) acts as a junction switch for emitter and collector circuits. When there is current flow in the base, flow is also possible between the emitter and collector. When the base is open, it stops emitter/collector flow. So when the points are closed in a contact-controlled transistorized system, the base allows current to flow from the ignition switch through the emitter and collector to the primary windings of the coil.

When the points open, the base circuit is turned off. This blocks current flow through the emitter/collector to the coil. As a result, the coil's primary field collapse and a surge of current is induced in the secondary windings.

Such contact-controlled transistorized ignition systems are considered superior to conventional points-type systems for several reasons: (1) Reduced voltage can be used in the circuit going from the points to the transistor base. This reduces arcing between the points and prolongs point life. (2) Higher-than-normal current can be used in the circuit going through the emitter/collector to the ignition coil. This produces higher secondary voltages and improves spark plug performance in difficult operating conditions.

However, these kinds of transistorized ignition systems still have

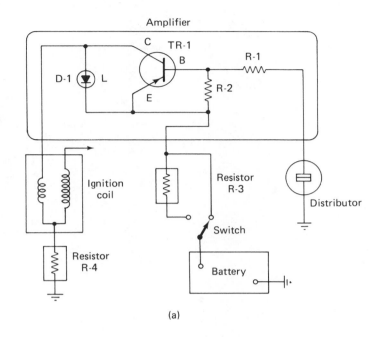

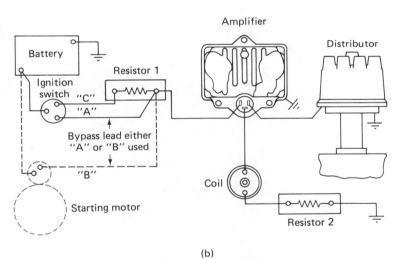

(b)

FIG. 9-2 (a) Internal wiring of typical circuit. (b) Typical circuit with built-in provision for bypassing resistor during cranking.

one failing. They rely on breaker points as the controlling switch. The point assembly, particularly the rubbing block, will wear out in time, even though arcing has been reduced. So manufacturers developed ignition control systems with no breaker points at all. They are called *breakerless* ignitions and eventually came to replace points-type systems altogether.

CAPACITOR DISCHARGE IGNITION SYSTEM

One of the first breakerless ignition systems was the capacitor discharge ignition (CDI). It replaces the points with a magnetic pulse distributor. This magnetic pulse unit signals a magnetic pulse amplifier (a collection of diodes, transistors, thyrsistors, resistors, and

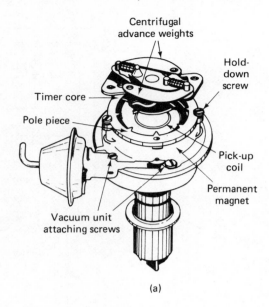

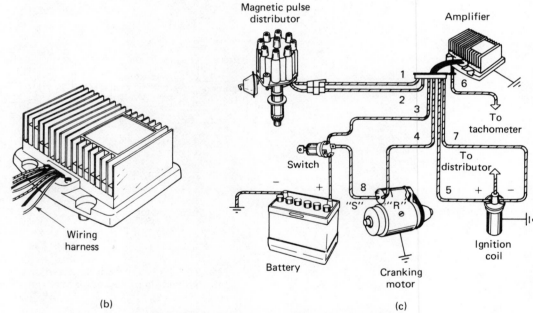

FIG. 9-3 (a) Partially exploded view of CDI distributor with cap removed. (b) Typical ignition pulse amplifier. (c) Typical wiring circuit with six-terminal connector on amplifier wiring harness.

capacitors) to discharge a momentary 300-V burst of electricity into the primary windings of the coil every time a spark plug is due to fire. When the field created by this pulsing discharge collapses, it induces current flow in the secondary windings to operate the spark plugs.

The main components of the magnetic pulse unit are a timer core, pole piece, pickup coil, and permanent magnet (Fig. 9-3). The timer core, sometimes called a reluctor, is attached to the distributor shaft and rotates with it, like the cam in a points-type system. The timer is shaped somewhat like a sprocket, with one tooth for each cylinder. Surrounding the timer core is a pole piece. It also resembles a sprocket, but one that has been turned inside out with the teeth pointing toward the center. The timer core and the pole piece have the same number of teeth. Whenever the teeth line up, a pulse of current is sent to the pulse amplifier, which in turn signals the capacitor to discharge into the coil's primary winding.

The current pulse is sent to the pulse amplifier because of the arrangement between the timer core, pole piece, permanent magnet, and pickup coil. This is how it works: The permanent magnet is attached to the pole piece. Its magnetic lines of force circle through the pole piece. When the teeth of the pole piece and timer core line up, the lines of force are able to pass between the two and become concentrated. When the teeth do not line up, the lines of force must pass through air and become dissipated (remember from Chapter 4 how lines of force prefer to pass through materials of high magnetic permeability). As a result, a pulsating magnetic field exists (Fig. 9-4). It is strongest when the teeth line up and weakest when they do not. These lines of force from the pulsating field cut across the pickup coil. As the lines of force balloon in and out, current flow is generated in the windings of the pickup coil. This current flow is not very great, but it is enough to signal the pulse amplifier, which supplies a corresponding but much greater flow of pulsating current to the primary windings of the ignition coil.

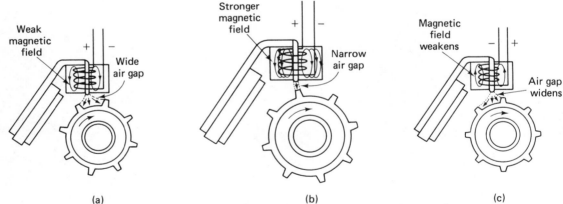

FIG. 9-4 Electronic ignition components. (a) Air gap offers resistance to field. (b) Increasing field strength induces positive voltage. (c) Magnetic field weakens again.

Centrifugal and mechanical spark advance are handled in a manner similar to earlier ignition systems. A vacuum advance unit is attached to the pole piece and magnetic pickup assembly. The assembly rotates back and forth in response to changes in manifold vacuum, advancing or retarding the spark as needed. The timer core is attached to centrifugal advance weights and rotates back and forth as engine speed changes. Dwell, however, is fixed, since there is no point gap to consider.

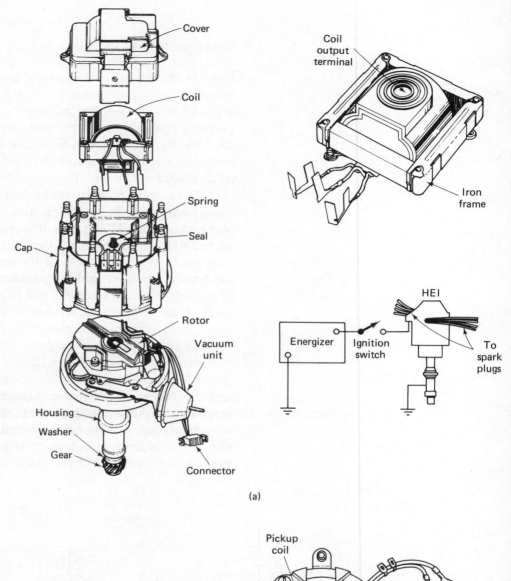

Cover

Coil

Spring

Seal

Cap

Rotor

Vacuum unit

Housing

Washer

Gear

Connector

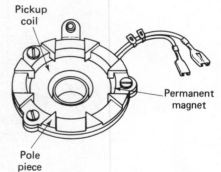

Coil output terminal

Iron frame

Energizer

Ignition switch

HEI

To spark plugs

(a)

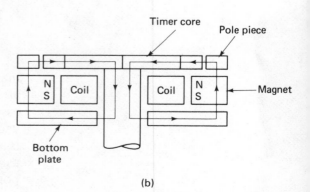

Pickup coil

Permanent magnet

Pole piece

Timer core

Pole piece

N S

Coil

Coil

N S

Magnet

Bottom plate

(b)

FIG. 9-5 High-energy ignition system: (a) H.E.I distributor assembly pickup coil.

**CURRENT ELECTRONIC
IGNITION SYSTEMS**

Most electronic ignition systems in use at the time of this writing are similar to the CDI unit just described. All contain a magnetic pulse distributor of some kind and all contain an amplifier unit which controls the primary flow to the ignition coil. (Although, as Chapter 11 reveals, manufacturers are now beginning to investigate computer controls of the primary circuit.) The principal difference is the capacitor discharge feature. Most pulse amplifiers in use today do not rely on a pulsating capacitor to operate the ignition coil. Instead, the amplifier unit is somewhat like a (very complicated) switch. It is normally "on," allowing current to flow into and saturate the primary windings of the ignition coil. It is turned off whenever a signal is received from the magnetic pulse distributor. This momentary interruption in the current flow to the coil's primary windings creates the high-energy surge from the secondary needed to fire the spark plugs.

General Motors high-energy ignition (HEI)

The basic operating components of this system are the same as those just described. The magnetic pulse distributor contains the same components as the CDI unit, and the pulse amplifier works as a switch to momentarily interrupt a normally "on" circuit going to the primary windings of the coil. However, the HEI unit appears differently because the ignition coil is located inside the distributor just beneath the cap. Figure 9-5 pictures a typical example.

Chrysler and Ford systems

The primary difference between Chrysler and Ford units and the GM system (aside from the location of the ignition coil) is the pole piece inside the magnetic pulse distributor. The GM pole piece surrounds the timer core with an equal number of internal teeth, whereas, the Chrysler and Ford pole piece only has one tooth or pickup point (Fig. 9-6). It works the same way as the previously described pole piece; whenever a timer core tooth passes the pickup point, a magnetic field is created. This field balloons in and out to induce current in the pickup coil. The pulsating current from the pickup coil signals the pulse amplifier to interrupt the flow to the primary coil windings.

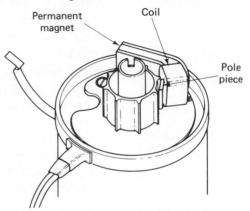

FIG. 9-6 Unit with one pickup point.

chapter

10

Electrical Schematics

INTRODUCTION Electrical schematics or wiring diagrams are confusing to many of us. When we look at one, we see lines running here and there in complicated patterns. If we try to trace current flow from the battery, we soon discover that the circuits branch off in every direction. It seems almost impossible to find a straight-line path from anywhere to anywhere else.

Yet, an electrical schematic can be almost as easy to use as an ordinary road map. They are similar in many ways. The main difference is one of familiarity. Imagine, for instance, how strange a road map would look if you had never seen one before. You would not know what the different symbols for roads, highways, town, and cities mean. You might not even be sure about the actual purpose of the road map; it would just be a jumble of lines. You are only able to use road maps because, over the years, you have become familiar with them.

This chapter will help you become familiar with electrical schematics. It will show you what an electrical schematic is and what is isn't, and it will give you some basic facts you need to properly understand a wiring diagram.

WHAT AN ELECTRICAL SCHEMATIC IS

An electrical schematic is a diagram or map of the components in an electrical system and the wires that run between the components. Like a road map, a wiring diagram shows you the size and nature of the routes traveled, the points connected by the routes, and the major intersections along the way. Trying to trace a problem in a car's electrical system without the aid of a wiring diagram is like trying to take a trip without a road map. You would do a lot of backtracking to find the correct path. You might even get lost.

WHAT AN ELECTRICAL SCHEMATIC ISN'T

Although an electrical schematic can do many things, there are some things it cannot do. It is important to remember what an electrical schematic isn't, if you are going to avoid being confused.

First, an electrical schematic, like a road map, is not a literal or physical picture of the area being surveyed. A road map does not show all the hills and curves along the way. An electrical schematic does not show all the twists and turns a wire must make going from one component to another. Nor does it show, in most cases, the components as they actually appear. An electrical schematic is a logical rather than a pictorial representation (Fig. 10-1). Components are shown only as symbols and the lines between the symbols simply tell you that the components are connected electrically. A certain wiring diagram may tell you: "One of the wires going from the right and left headlights is a light-tan-colored number 16." It doesn't tell you that for most of its travel the wire is hidden in a wrapped harness which itself is obscured by the radiator shroud.

Besides knowing that a wiring diagram is a logical rather than a pictorial representation, it is also important to remember this point: You cannot visualize or "see" an entire automotive electrical schematic at one time.

Some people, when they look at a schematic, become confused because they can't get an overall picture of all the different paths and connectors. What they don't realize is that nobody can maintain such a mental image (Fig. 10-2). Again, it is like reading a road map. When you are trying to chart a route from one place to another, you don't try to memorize or "see" all the roads on the map. Instead, you concentrate on the roads that will take you from where you are to where you want to go. The trick to using either an electrical schematic or a road map is to ignore the information you don't need at the moment.

FACTS NEEDED FOR A PROPER APPROACH TO ELECTRICAL SCHEMATICS

Beside knowing generally what an electrical schematic is and what it isn't, there are also some specific facts you need to bear in mind before you can properly approach a wiring diagram.

1. Just as a road map is divided into certain political or physical units (states, counties, cities, etc.), an automotive electrical system is

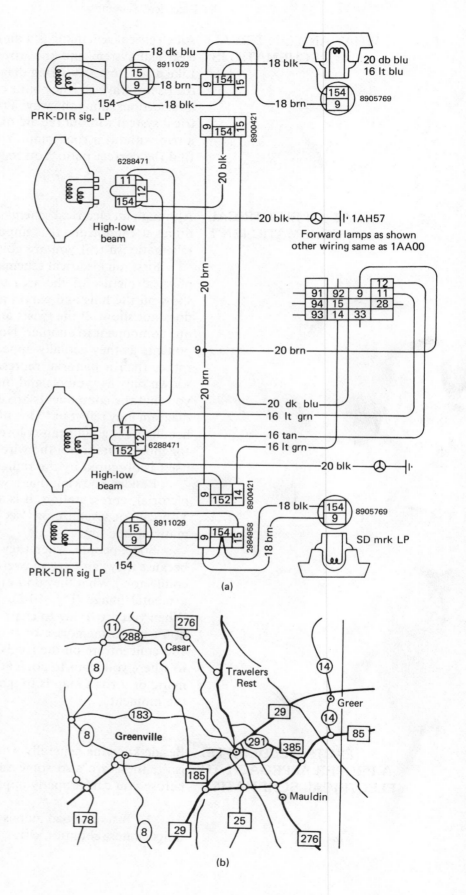

FIG. 10-1 The headlight circuit pictured in (a) is like the section of a roadmap pictured in (b). Both are logical rather than literal representations.

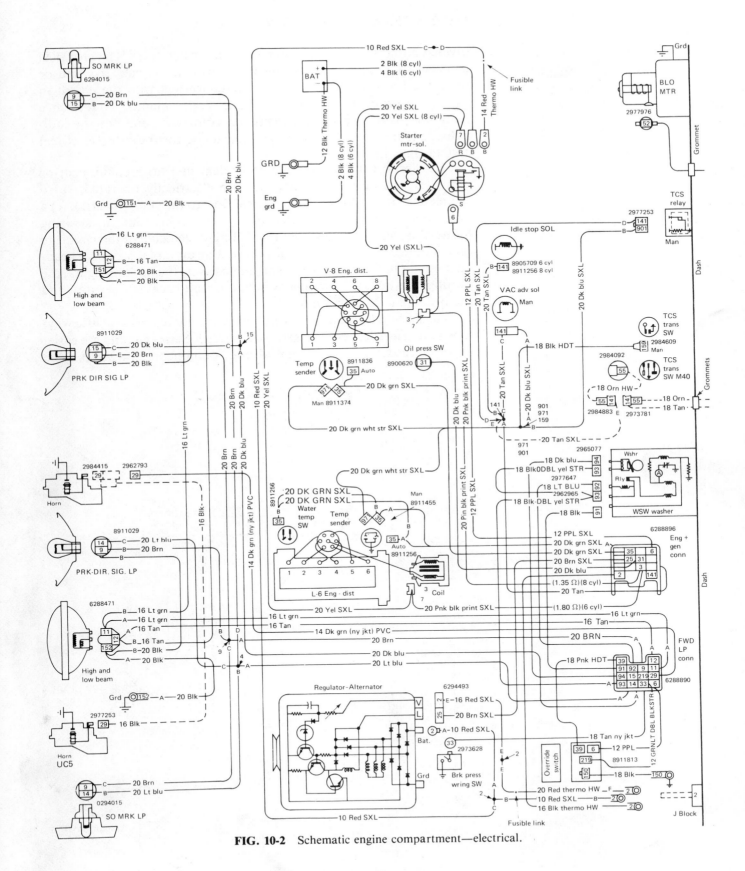

FIG. 10-2 Schematic engine compartment—electrical.

divided into certain circuits. In most cases, when there is an electrical problem, it is something wrong in a particular circuit. To find or solve the problem, you need only be concerned with the circuit in which the problem lies. Usually, your service manual or reference book will help by providing separate wiring diagrams for the individual circuits as well as an overall schematic for the entire electrical system (Fig. 10-3).

A circuit usually has four basic elements: (a) a component or group of related components that are electrically operated, (b) a switch or switches to control electrical flow to the component(s), (c) a protective device such as a fuse or circuit breaker, and (d) a wiring harness to electrically connect the different elements in the circuit to one another and to a source of power. For example, a typical headlight circuit includes the headlights themselves, the parking lights, the headlight switch, the dimmer switch, a circuit breaker (or fuse), and the headlight wiring harness.

2. As you learned in previous chapters, there are two basic ways to wire an electrical circuit: series or parallel. Series circuits are easier to visualize but do not prevent all the components in a series from

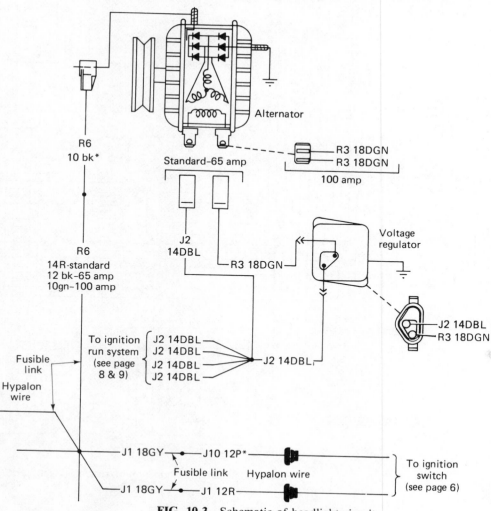

FIG. 10-3 Schematic of headlight circuit.

failing if only one fails. Parallel circuits, which present a more complicated schematic, allow one component to fail without affecting other components in the circuit. For this reason, automotive electrical wiring is mostly of the parallel kind. The principal exceptions are switches and circuit protectors (fuses, etc.). They must be wired in series with the components they operate or protect. Otherwise, they couldn't function.

3. There is a heirarchy or order among the switches in an automobile's electrical system. In other words, some switches control the power flow to other switches. For example, the position of the ignition switch determines whether certain other switches receive power and are thus able to control the components they are connected to. Unless the ignition switch is in the "run" or "ACC" position, the radio, fan blower, and turn signal switches in most cars will not receive power. However, the headlights and emergency flasher switches are usually connected to separate circuits and will operate regardless of the position of the ignition switch. It is important to know about this hierarchy of switches when you are troubleshooting a circuit because you may have to test several switches in order to find the problem.

4. Most of the car's wiring is hidden inside harnesses. They are simply collections of wires wrapped or covered with plastic sheaths that provide protection and support for the wires they contain. Usually, there are one or more harnesses for the electrically operated devices in the engine compartment, a harness for the dash instruments and accessories, a long harness running along the frame or chassis from the front to the rear of the car, and a separate harness at the rear of the car for the taillights, turn signals, and so on.

5. In most cases, the harnesses do not need to be disturbed for electrical testing or repair. That is usually accomplished at the end connectors where the harnesses ae joined. Almost all modern cars use connectors of the "quick-disconnect" or snap-apart variety. The only time a harness need be disassembled is when testing at both ends of a wire indicates that it is broken or open inside the harness.

6. As a general rule, most electrical schematics show where quick-disconnect junctions are located. They also show another kind of connection. If you look at the wiring diagram included in this chapter, you will see small black dots where some of the wires cross. These black dots indicate electrical junctions. Junctions like these are usually hidden inside the wiring harness and are not meant to be taken apart or examined unless testing at the quick-disconnect points indicates a problem at one of the nondetachable junctions.

7. There is one final point to be remembered. An automotive electrical schematic only shows half the electrical flow path in the car's electrical system. The ground return circuits are not pictured. So if you see a component with the electrical symbol for ground leading away from it, you know that electricity flows from the component, through the car's metal parts, back to the negative terminal of the battery. If the component (often a switch) does *not* have a ground symbol, one of the wires connected to the device must deliver current and the other must take it away.

chapter
11

Electronic Engine Control Systems

INTRODUCTION   This chapter introduces the latest automotive electrical devices . . . the on-board computers, sensors, solenoids, circuits, and so on, that directly control ignition timing and air/fuel mixture. After looking at considerations common to all manufacturers, the particular hardware and approaches employed by Chrysler, GM, and Ford will be examined.

BASIC CONSIDERATIONS   Air/fuel mixture and ignition timing are two keys to the operation of any internal combustion engine. To achieve the best balance between power, driveability, economy, and emissions, the air and fuel must be mixed in just the right proportions and must be ignited at just the right time. If all engines operated at the same speed, under the same conditions, an "ideal" balance might not be too difficult to obtain. Unfortunately, that is not the case.

First, certain fuel ratios and ignition conditions tend to favor one aspect of engine operation over another. For instance, relatively rich mixtures generally provide better power and driveability, whereas leaner mixtures, up to the point of misfiring, give better fuel economy and reduced emissions. Also, changing engine speeds and climatic conditions tend to alter air/fuel ratios and ignition conditions. These changes, in turn, upset the balance among power, driveability, economy, and emissions. So any approach to maintaining air/fuel mixture and proper ignition must not only take into account changing conditions, but also the particular aspect of engine operation being favored.

For a number of years, mechanical devices in the carburetor and distributor have been used to assure the fuel mixture and ignition process. Up until the middle to late 1960s, these devices worked well because the primary emphasis was on driveability and power. Engines operated on relatively rich mixtures which were fairly easy to maintain. Since fuel was cheap and air pollution was not yet regulated, designers didn't have to be as concerned about economy and emissions. The mechanical systems were adequate to handle two parts of the four-part equation among power, driveability, economy, and emissions.

Even after emission control became a factor in the late 1960s and early 1970s, the mechanical systems remained adequate. Power and driveability did suffer because of leaner mixtures and other internal and external engine changes. However, driveability was not that bad and it was always possible to make engines larger to compensate for the power loss. And despite the fact that larger, pollution-control engines of the period used more fuel, the operating costs were still within the range of most people. There was no need yet to make any basic changes in the mechanical systems used to monitor and adjust air/fuel mixtures and ignition timing.

Then, in the middle to late 1970s, a number of significant events took place:

1. Fuel costs rose dramatically, because of political conditions in the Middle East and increased consumption plus inflation at home.
2. The federal government passed legislation requiring manufacturers to produce more fuel-efficient vehicles.
3. Pollution controls became even more rigid.
4. The cost and size of computers decreased while their power and capacity increased.

So, for the first time, all factors in the equation had to be given equal weight. Engineers had to design smaller engines for smaller cars, and still provide adequate power, good driveability, improved economy, and reduced emissions.

One solution has been to rely more and more on electronic systems. We saw one example of this in Chapter 10, the solid-state ignition systems. These devices, which became common in the middle 1970s, were designed to produce "hotter" ignition sparking that allowed engines to run on leaner fuel mixtures.

The problem is that even with hotter, solid-state ignition systems, lean mixtures are difficult to control. Slight changes in engine temperature, air temperature, engine speed, and so on, can shift the equation into the misfiring range, where power, driveability, economy, and emissions all suffer. To avoid that, it becomes necessary to make almost instant changes in timing and fuel mixture.

This is where the new generation of low-cost, high-powered computers enter the picture. Instead of using mechanical devices to sense changing conditions and make compensating adjustments, manufacturers are beginning to rely on electronic brains to do the job. At the time of this writing, all three of the major U.S. automakers provide at least one engine with computer controls.

Typically, one of these computers receives information (concerning speed, temperature, etc.) from sensors located about the vehicle. Then the computer analyzes the information, deciding exactly what the timing and/or fuel mixture needs to be. After that, the computer sends control signals to the distributor, fuel induction system, or both.

Various types of systems are in use at the present time. Some control just the distributor. Others control a modified, but still fairly conventional carburetor. Still others control both the distributor and a new type of fuel-injection system. At least one manufacturer has provided a computer with built-in troubleshooting features.

The remainder of this chapter discusses these various systems.

1. *What are two keys to the operation of any internal combustion engine?*

2. *What must be taken into account in any approach to maintaining the air/fuel mixture and proper ignition timing?*

3. *Mechanical devices in the distributor and carburetor were first used to assure fuel mixture and ignition timing. Why did these devices work well up to the middle to late 1960s and remain adequate up into the 1970s?*

4. *What events took place in the middle to late 1970s that prompted the development of computer-controlled systems?*

5. *Where do automotive computers receive information, and what do they do with it once it is received?*

CHRYSLER LEAN BURN SYSTEM

Chrysler was the first major U.S. automaker to employ an on-board computer control system. Called the Lean Burn System (Fig. 11-1), it consists of a number of input devices (sensors located about the engine) and a small computer mounted on the air cleaner housing. The traditional vacuum and centrifugal timing advance mechanisms in the distributor are replaced by direct computer controls.

Chrysler claims that its Lean Burn engines operate at an air/fuel ratio of 18:1. At this level, nitric oxide pollutants in the exhaust are sharply reduced. However, in conventional engines, hydrocarbons and carbon monoxides tend to rise as the air/fuel mixture goes over 15:1—into what would normally be the misfiring range.

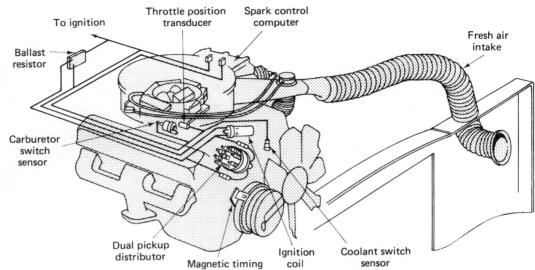

To ignition

Throttle position transducer

Spark control computer

Fresh air intake

Ballast resistor

Carburetor switch sensor

Dual pickup distributor

Magnetic timing

Ignition coil

Coolant switch sensor

FIG. 11-1 Pictorial sketch of electronic Lean Burn System.

Chrysler avoids the problem by retarding the ignition timing. This increases the temperature throughout the exhaust systems, which helps to oxidize hydrocarbons and carbon monoxide. In effect, the entire exhaust system becomes a working part of the emission control apparatus.

Like other manufacturers, Chrysler adopted computerized systems primarily because of the difficulty of controlling the lean-burning, retarded-spark engines. Conventional vacuum/centrifugal mechanisms do not respond with sufficient speed or precision to changing conditions. Nor does the fixed advance curve of these control devices give the range of adjustment needed.

Sensors (input devices)

The following input devices (see Fig. 11-2) sense changing engine conditions, convert the information into electrical signals, then transmit the signals to the on-board computer.

1. *Coolant temperature sensor*, mounted in the liquid coolant passages, informs the computer of the engine temperature.

2. *Ambient air temperature sensor*, located near the computer itself, provides information about the temperature of the air going into the engine.

3. *Throttle transducer*, located on the right corner of the carburetor, translates the position of the throttle (part open, fully open, etc.) into electrical signals and transmits the signals to the computer.

4. *Carburetor switch*, located at the end of the throttle, lets the computer know if the throttle is in the idle position.

5. *Distributor pick-up coils*, located within the distributor, provide spark timing signals to the computer. These mag-

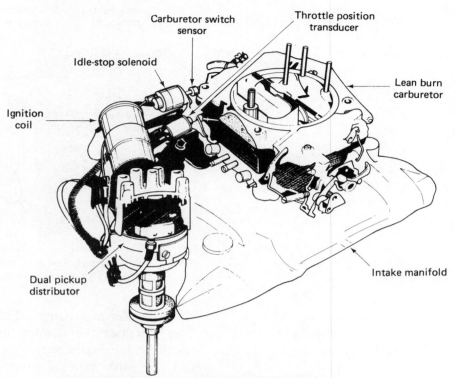

FIG. 11-2 Sketch of intake manifold, carburetor, ignition coil, carburetor sensor, throttle transducer, and dual pickup distributor.

netic, induction-type coils produce electrical impulses in a similar manner to the pickup coils used in conventional, solid-state ignition systems. The difference is that the signals are advanced or retarded by the computer instead of by vacuum and centrifugal advance mechanisms built into the distributor. In other words, after the signals are sent to the computer, it decides what the timing ought to be, then interrupts the primary flow to the ignition coil. The resulting, high-voltage secondary surges flow to the distributor, to be routed to the appropriate spark plugs in a conventional manner.

Chrysler provides two of these pickup coils (Fig. 11-3). One, called the Start Pick-Up, provides a signal for starting. The Run Pick-Up coil produces the signal used for regular operation.

Computer functions (output)

The principal output of the Chrysler computer is the spark timing information, relayed, via interruptions in the primary ignition circuit, to the ignition coil. The Program Schedule Module of the computer receives and interprets information from the sensors. The Ignition Control Module directs the operation of the ignition coil, acting on information relayed from the Program Module.

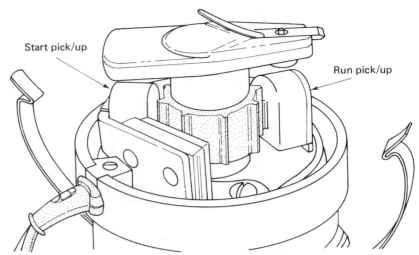

FIG. 11-3 Pictorial sketch of dual pickup distributor showing "start" and "run" pickup coils.

1. Who was the first major U.S. automaker to employ on-board computer controls?

2. Does the Lean Burn System contain traditional vacuum and centrifugal timing advance mechanisms?

3. What is the air/fuel ratio claimed for the Lean Burn System?

4. What problems with pollutants occur at that air/fuel ratio?

5. How does this manufacturer get around the problem?

6. Name the input sensors in the Lean Burn System.

7. Which sensors provide basic timing signals to the computer?

8. What does the computer do with these signals? Where are they relayed?

9. What is the principal output of the computer?

GENERAL MOTORS C-4 SYSTEM

The GM system uses a computer to adjust the air/fuel mixture directly in the carburetor (Fig. 11-4). The objective is to keep the air/fuel ratio in a relatively narrow range (about 14.7:1). According to GM, this maximizes the efficiency of the Three Way Catalytic Converter, allowing it to reduce nitric oxide, carbon monoxide, and hydrocarbon pollutants to lower levels.

The system employs modified versions of the E4M Quadrajet and Rochester Dualjet 210 carburetors (relabeled E4ME and E2ME, respectively). Each contains two specially stepped metering rods in the main fuel jets. Attached to the plunger of a computer-controlled solenoid, the rods pulse up and down 10 times per second (Fig. 11-5). The exact position of the rods at any given time (determined by the solenoid) decides how much fuel enters the engine. Air flow to the carburetor idle circuit is determined by an air bleed valve located in

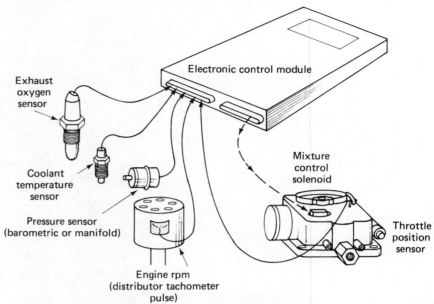

FIG. 11-4   Pictorial sketch of GM C-4 system.

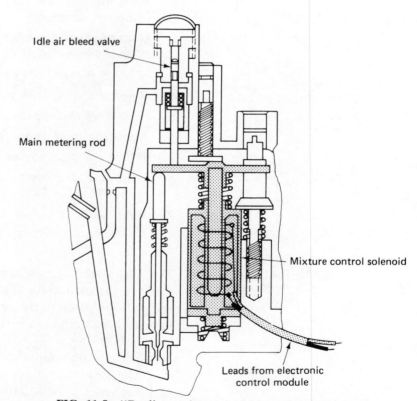

FIG. 11-5   "Dueljet: carburetor mixture control solenoid.

the air horn. The position of the valve is also controlled by the solenoid (and hence the computer).

The computer or Electronic Control Module (ECM) (Fig. 11-6) decides how rich or lean the mixture must be by evaluating information provided by the sensors on the following factors (see Fig. 11-7):

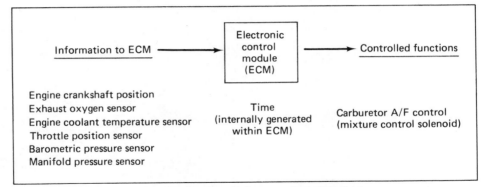

FIG. 11-6   Electronic control module features.

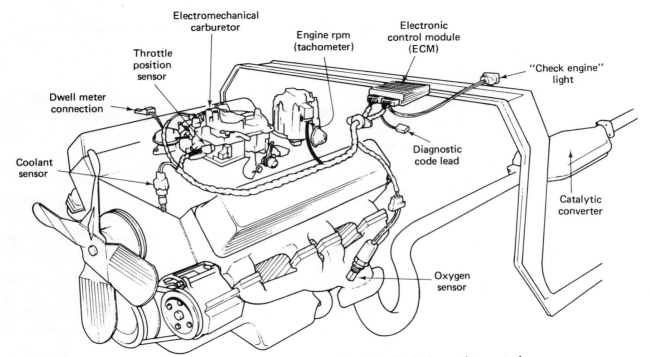

FIG. 11-7   Air/fuel metering control.

1.   Exhaust oxygen.
2.   Coolant temperature.
3.   Air pressure (both manifold and atmospheric).
4.   Engine r/min.

1.   *Does the computer in the GM C-4 system adjust both air/fuel mixture and ignition timing? If not, which does it control?*
2.   *What is the principal objective of the C-4 system?*
3.   *What computer-controlled elements in the modified carburetors are used in the C-4 system?*
4.   *What is the ECM?*
5.   *What information is provided to the ECM?*

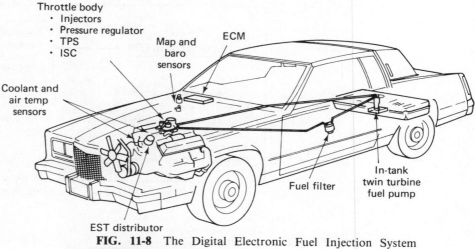

FIG. 11-8 The Digital Electronic Fuel Injection System (DEFI) components.

GM DEFI SYSTEM   The GM Digital Electronic Fuel Injection (DEFI) system (Fig. 11-8) provides computer-controlled ignition, fuel injection, idle speed control, and built-in troubleshooting. The following are the major elements of the system:

1. Electronic Control Module (ECM).
2. Sensors (similar to the ones used in the C-4 system, plus a throttle position sensor).
3. Electronic fuel injection (including fuel pump, pressure regulator, injectors, air induction controls, etc.).
4. Electronic distributor.
5. Idle speed control actuator.
6. Systems diagnostic readout display panel on the dash.

Sensors

The ECM computer receives information from the following sensors:

1. Manifold Air Temperature Sensor (MAT): a thermister (resistance thermometer) located in the intake manifold.
2. Engine Coolant Temperature Sensor (CTS): mounted just below the engine thermostat, provides the ECM with information needed to adjust ignition timing, idle speed, and fuel enrichment during cold operation (thus replacing the choke on a conventional carburetor).
3. Manifold Absolute Pressure Sensor (MAP): signals changes in manifold pressure, giving the ECM the information it needs to richen or lean out the mixture as load and speed change.
4. Barometric Pressure Sensor (BARO): signals changes in atmospheric pressure due to weather conditions, thus allow-

ing the ECM to make compensating changes in the injector action.

5. Throttle Position Sensor (TPS): a variable rheostat attached to the end of the throttle shaft. The TPS signals the throttle position to the computer, which uses the information to help decide the conditions for idle speed control.

6. Electronic Spark Timing Distributor (EST): containing a magnetic induction type of coil that sends signals to the ECM computer. These signals are used to calculate engine speed as well as to provide a basis for setting the ignition timing.

As the ECM receives signals from these sources, it sends out operating instructions to the fuel injection system, distributor, and idle speed mechanism.

Air/fuel induction system

The heart of the DEFI fuel system (Figs. 11-9 and 11-10) consists of two fuel injectors positioned above a throttle body mounted on the intake manifold. Each injector contains a solenoid plunger mechanism. When the solenoid is energized by a signal from the ECM, the plunger rises, permitting a spring-loaded ball valve to lift off its seat, thus causing fuel to squirt under pressure into the air stream.

When the engine is first started, both plungers squirt simultaneously. After that, during normal running, they operate alternately, first one, then the other. The rate of operation is controlled by the ECM as it receives and evaluates signals from the sensors located about the engine.

Fuel for the injectors is delivered by a turbine-type pump positioned in the fuel tank. The fuel is routed through a filter to a pressure regulator in the throttle body. The regulator employs a diaphragm

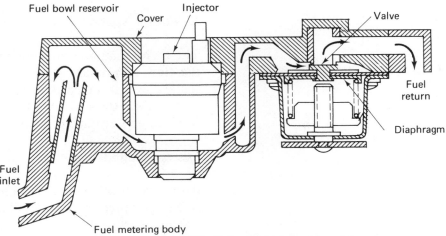

FIG. 11-9 Fuel pressure regulator.

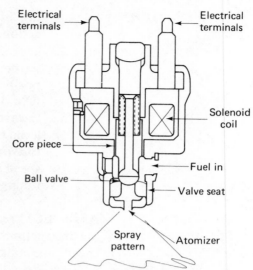

FIG. 11-10   Cross section of fuel injector.

relief valve and a preloaded spring to maintain fuel pressure at 10.5 psi across the injector nozzle inlets. Fuel not required to maintain that pressure is sent back to the fuel tank.

The volume of air flowing into the intake manifold (and hence, engine speed) is controlled by two throttle plates located in two bores in the throttle body. The throttle plates are connected in a conventional manner by a throttle linkage to the accelerator pedal. The position of the throttle, as noted before, is monitored by the TPS sensor.

Idle speed control

When the TPS sensor tells the EMS computer that the throttle is closed, the computer relays signals to a small motor connected to the throttle linkage. This reversible electric motor is called the Idle Speed Control Actuator (ICS). It acts as a movable idle stop, adjusting the idle to the exact position required by the conditions existing at any given moment.

Electronic spark timing

The ECM computer controls spark advance by directly interrupting the flow of primary current to the ignition coil. The basic timing signal comes from a pickup coil in the distributor. After being received by the EMS, the signal is advanced or retarded, depending on signals received and evaluated from other sensors.

System diagnostics

Besides controlling the operation of the fuel and ignition systems, the ECM computer can also troubleshoot problems that occur in these systems, particularly those involving malfunctioning sensors.

If a problem occurs, the message "check engine" appears on a dash-mounted information dislplay panel. This lets the operator know that something is wrong. When the car is brought to a mechanic, he turns the ignition switch on, leaves it on for 5 seconds, then simultaneously presses the Off and Warmer buttons on the climate control panel. He holds the buttons in until the numbers "00" appear on the dash information display. After that, numbered troubleshooting codes will be displayed. The mechanic uses these codes to locate the appropriate printed troubleshooting chart. If more than one problem exists, the mechanic repeats the procedure so that the next highest troubleshooting code will be displayed on the information panel.

1. *What aspects of engine operation are controlled in the DEFI system?*

2. *What are the principal elements of the system?*

3. *Name the six sensors used in the DEFI system.*

4. *What is the heart of the DEFI air/fuel induction system?*

5. *What is the difference in injector action when the engine is first started and after it is running?*

6. *How is engine speed (above idle) controlled in the DEFI system?*

7. *How is idle speed controlled?*

8. *What controls spark timing?*

9. *What additional feature is provided by the DEFI system?*

FORD ELECTRONIC ENGINE CONTROL II (EECII) SYSTEM

The Ford EECII system (Fig. 11-11) uses the Electronic Control Assembly (ECA) computer to directly control ignition timing, air/fuel mixture, thermactor air flow (exhaust gas recirculation), and idle speed.

The system receives information from seven sensors (see Fig. 11-12):

1. Barometric Pressure (BP) and Manifold Absolute Pressure (MAP) Sensor: contained in a single housing.
2. Engine Coolant Temperature (ECT) Sensor.
3. Crankshaft Position (CP) Sensor: a four-lobe pulse ring mounted on the crankshaft damper, it provides the ECA computer with the basic information needed for setting the ignition timing. This is different from Chrysler and GM systems, which use a magnetic induction coil in the distributor to provide timing signals.
4. Throttle Position (TP) Sensor.
5. EGR Valve Position (EVP) Sensor.
6. Exhaust Gas Oxygen (EGO) Sensor.

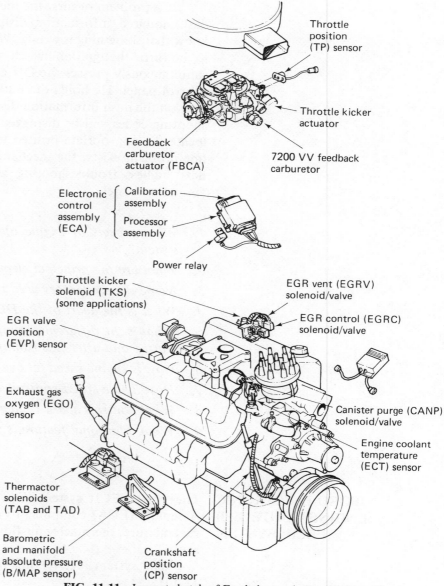

FIG. 11-11 Layout sketch of Ford electronic Engine Control II (EEC II) System.

Acting on the information received from these sensors, the ECA computer sends output signals to these control units:

1. Feedback Carburetor Actuator (FBCA): to adjust the air/fuel mixture (Fig. 11-13).
2. Ignition Control Module: to relay spark timing signals to the ignition coil.
3. EGR Control Solenoids: to direct air flow to the thermactor unit.
4. Canister Purge Solenoids: to control the recirculation of trapped fuel vapors.

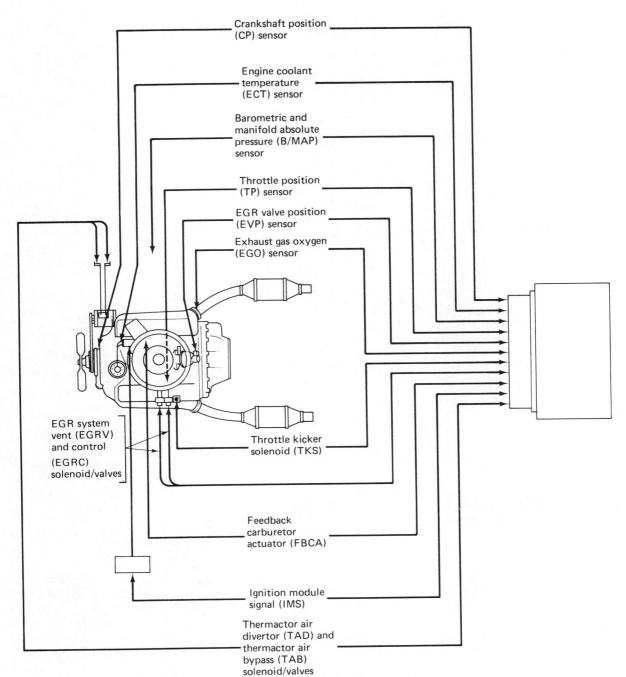

Crankshaft position
(CP) sensor

Engine coolant
temperature
(ECT) sensor

Barometric and
manifold absolute
pressure (B/MAP)
sensor

Throttle position
(TP) sensor

EGR valve position
(EVP) sensor

Exhaust gas oxygen
(EGO) sensor

EGR system
vent (EGRV)
and control
(EGRC)
solenoid/valves

Throttle kicker
solenoid (TKS)

Feedback
carburetor
actuator (FBCA)

Ignition module
signal (IMS)

Thermactor air
divertor (TAD) and
thermactor air
bypass (TAB)
solenoid/valves

FIG. 11-12 Operational diagram of (EEC II) System.

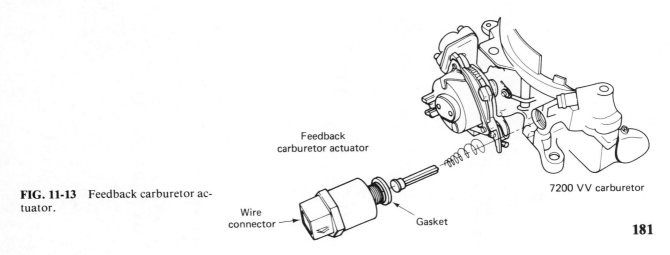

FIG. 11-13 Feedback carburetor actuator.

Feedback
carburetor actuator

7200 VV carburetor

Wire
connector

Gasket

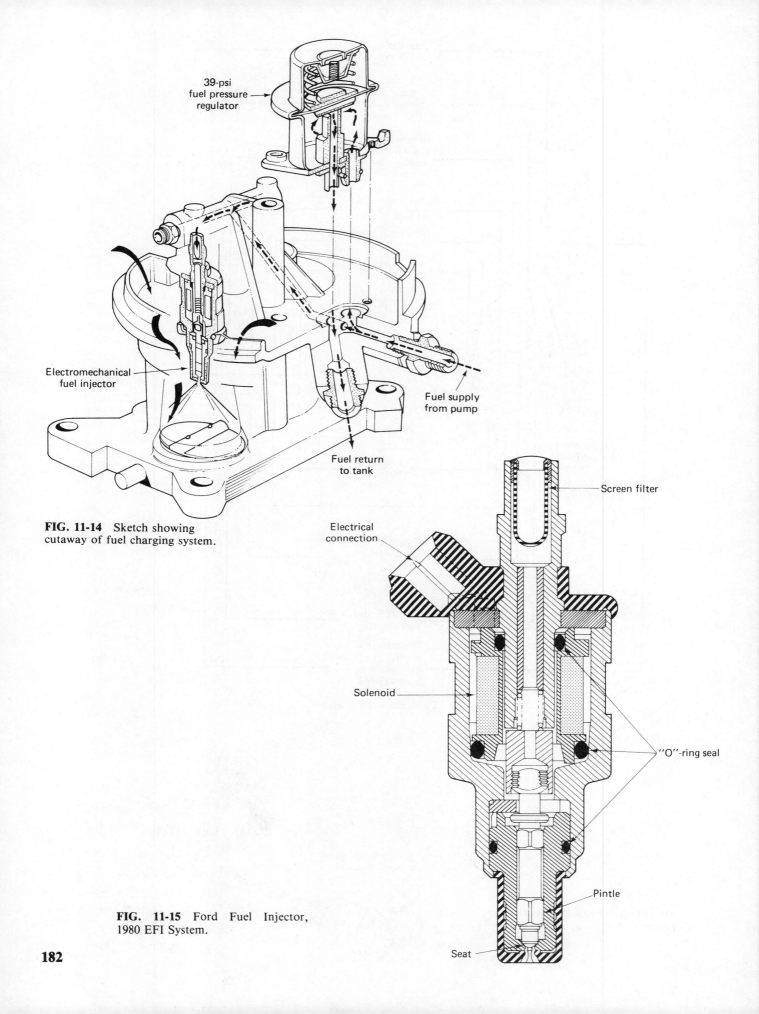

FIG. 11-14 Sketch showing cutaway of fuel charging system.

39-psi fuel pressure regulator

Electromechanical fuel injector

Fuel supply from pump

Fuel return to tank

Screen filter

Electrical connection

Solenoid

"O"-ring seal

Pintle

Seat

FIG. 11-15 Ford Fuel Injector, 1980 EFI System.

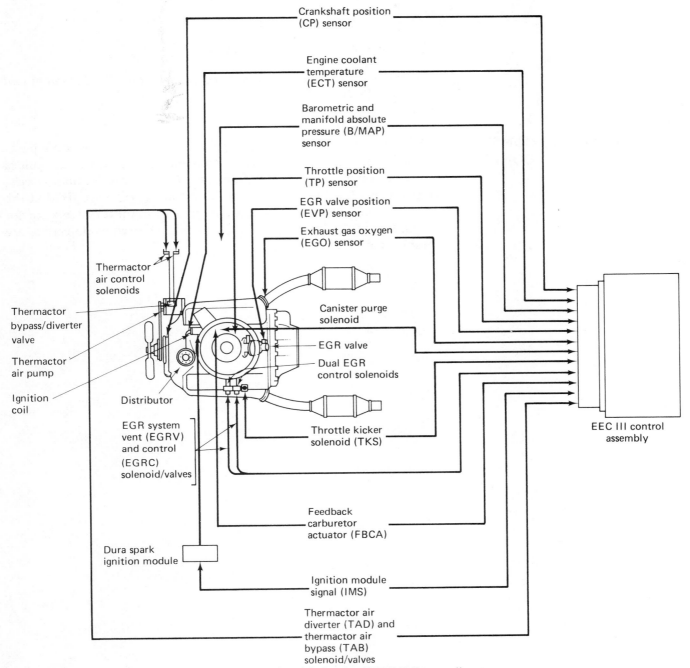

FIG. 11-16 Pictorial sketch of EEC II System diagram.

5. Throttle Kicker Solenoid: to control idle speed.
6. Thermactor Solenoids: to participate in thermactor action.

1. What does ECA stand for?
2. What does the ECA control?
3. Name the input and output devices in the EECII system.

FORD ELECTRONIC ENGINE CONTROL III (EECIII) SYSTEM

The Ford EECIII system (Figs. 11-14 to 11-16) is similar to the EECII system, with one exception. The EECIII system uses fuel injection instead of a carburetor. Two solenoid-actuated, computer-controlled injectors are mounted over two accelerator-pedal-controlled throttle plates.

1. *What is the principal difference between the EECII system and the EECIII system?*

SERVICING COMPUTER CONTROLS

All of the computer control devices described in the preceding paragraphs are sensitive, delicate instruments. Manufacturers' guides must be followed exactly to troubleshoot problems. In many cases, adjustments (air/fuel mixture, ignition timing, etc.) are fixed at the time of manufacture. And many components in these systems are not repairable at the local level. Parts, once diagnosed as defective, are simply replaced.

section
2

Service Sampler

service sampler

Test Equipment

Suppose that a headlight goes out in a car, or two headlights, or both tail lights, or the radio? Finding the problem requires a trip through the car's circuitry. To properly take such a trip, you need a roadmap (a circuit diagram) and the correct tools. This exercise introduces you to the operation of some electrical test tools.

JUMPER WIRE The simplest piece of electrical test equipment is a jumper wire or cable (Fig. A-1). It is nothing much more than a section of stranded, insulated wire with connections at each end. By substituting a jumper wire for a section of circuit, you can get some idea if that particular part of the circuit is working.

Suppose that you have a car whose headlights aren't burning. To quickly check the operation of the headlight switch, you could connect the jumper wire to the appropriate terminals on either side of the switch. This, in effect, would short the switch out by providing an alternate flow path around it. If the lights burn now, you know the switch had been at fault. If they don't burn, the problem still *could* be in the switch, but there would have to be some other fault in the circuit as well.

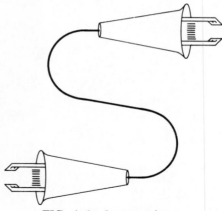

FIG. A-1   Jumper wire.

TEST LIGHTS   A test light is like a jumper wire with a small light bulb attached. The bulb (by shining or not shining) lets you know whether a section of circuit has current or if it will let current flow through. There are two kinds of test lights, those that contain their own power source and those that rely on an outside source of power (such as the car's own electrical system).

Self-powered test lights (Fig. A-2) are used to determine the continuity of circuits—in other words, to determine if the circuit is complete so that current can flow through. To see how this is done, suppose that the electric windshield wipers in your car are not working. To test the wiper motor for continuity with a self-powered test light (Fig. A-3), you would first isolate the motor from its power source (the battery) by disconnecting the motor at its positive terminal. Then you would connect one of the test lights leads to the positive motor terminal and the other lead to ground. If the motor's circuit is complete, current from the test light's battery should go from the positive terminal, through the motor's circuitry to ground, and then back to the test light to complete the circuit and cause the test light to shine. If the test light doesn't shine, the circuit is broken somewhere between the positive terminal and the motor's ground point.

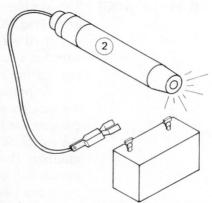

FIG. A-2   Self-powered test light for continuity checking.

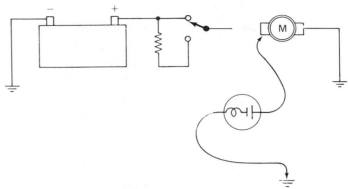

FIG. A-3 Test equipment: Self-powered test light.

A nonpowered test light (Fig. A-4) is strictly a jumper wire with a light bulb attached. It is used to check continuity and power. Continuity with a nonpowered test light (Figs. A-5 and A-6) is typically determined by separating a circuit into two segments and attaching one test light lead to the loose end of the positive side (the side nearest the battery's positive terminal) and the other lead to ground. If the circuit is complete up to the point of separation, current will flow through the test light, causing it to shine.

Suppose, in the previous example, you determined that the windshield wiper motor's internal circuitry was complete even though the motor still wasn't working. To check the circuit leading

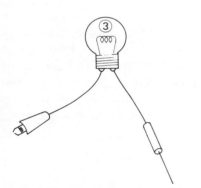

FIG. A-4 Nonpowered test light.

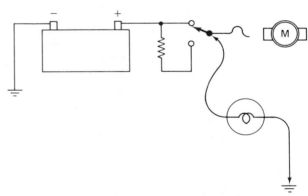

FIG. A-5 Test equipment: Nonpowered test light.

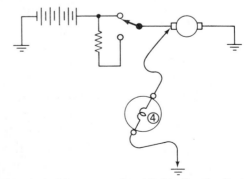

FIG. A-6 Nonpowered test light: Continuity test.

up to the motor with an externally powered test light, you would first remove the wire at the motor's positive terminal. Then you would connect one test lead to the loose end of the wire and the other end to ground. If the circuit is complete up to this point, the test light should shine when the ignitions switch and wiper's switch are turned on. If the light doesn't shine, you would know that the circuit is open somewhere from the battery's positive terminal up to the motor's positive terminal.

In the continuity test just described, the test light was hooked up in series. All the current had to flow through the tester. However, in a typical test for power, nothing need be disconnected because the tester is attached parallel to the circuit. Power (if it is flowing) will go through the tester as well as the circuit.

For example, you could quickly determine if the wiper's motor is receiving power by connecting one of the test light leads to the motor's positive terminal and the other lead to ground. If power is flowing up to the positive terminal, it will also pass through the test light, causing it to shine. If there is no power, you would work your way back along the circuit until you find a point that has power. Then you would know that the open circuit occurs somewhere between that point and the last location tested.

Note: Because modern terminals and connections limit direct access to wiring, you might wish to start your search at the fuse block and work backwards toward the motor, testing at the access points provided.

As you may have noticed, these simple test devices have somewhat overlapping functions. All are used basically to determine gross electrical malfunctions, whether a circuit is opened and closed, and if it is open where the break occurs. To perform more precise testing you must use a test meter: an ammeter, voltmeter, or ohmmeter. These devices tell you how much current is flowing, at what pressure, and encountering what resistance along the way.

TEST METER CONSTRUCTION

Most ammeters, voltmeters, and ohmmeters have similar components. They usually contain a permanent magnet and an electromagnet with a needle attached (Fig. A-7). The electromagnet is connected to the test leads that are attached to the circuit being tested. The strength of the electromagnet varies according to the current passing through. When the current flow is great (which is related to voltage and resistance), the electromagnet causes the attached needle to register high. When the current flow is low, the needle registers on the low side.

Whether a meter is an ammeter, voltmeter, or ohmmeter depends on its internal circuitry and the way it is connected to the circuit being tested. As you might imagine, some of the more expensive devices

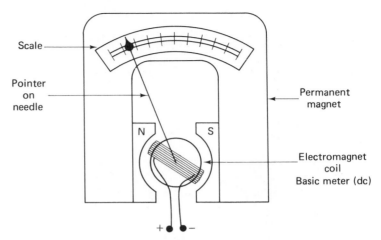

FIG. A-7 Meter construction.

combine all these functions into one instrument. However, even if a given tester is only able to read amps, volts or ohms, you can, by remembering the relationships given in Ohm's Law, determine what the other quantities will be. In fact, much automotive electrical testing is of this nature—relating readings in volts or amps to resistance.

Ammeters

An ammeter is used to measure amperage, the amount of current passing through a circuit. This information in automotive testing is often employed to determine the presence of short circuits or excessive resistance. A short circuit is often indicated if the current flowing through a particular circuit segment is higher than the specified amperage. This happens if two wires touch where they shouldn't, allowing current from the one circuit to be added to the circuit being tested.

When the amperage reading is lower than specifications, the problem is likely to be excessive resistance. The excessive resistance could be caused by a frayed or damaged wire, or by corroded or loose terminals.

Ammeters are connected in series so that all the current in a particular circuit flows through the tester [Fig. A-8(b)]. If you wanted to check the current flowing through a particular electrical circuit and component of an automobile, you could detach the lead wire to the circuit, then connect one ammeter test lead to the wire just disconnected and the other test lead to the positive battery post. With all the appropriate switches turned on, you could then read the amount of current flowing in that circuit.

Note: Some ammeters now use an inductive-type pickup. This is a clamp that goes around a wire to provide a quick, easy reading of the current flowing through the wire.

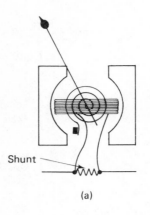

Shunt

(a)

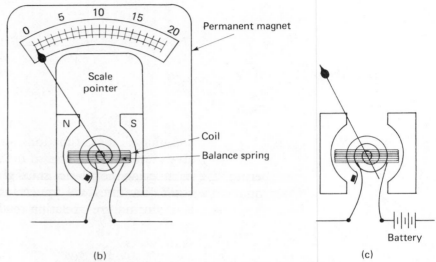

Permanent magnet

Scale pointer

N   S

Coil

Balance spring

Battery

(b)   (c)

FIG. A-8 (a) Ammeter circuit. (b) Voltmeter circuit. (c) Ohmmeter circuit.

An ammeter can also serve as a continuity tester. If an ammeter scale shows current flow, then the particular section of circuit being tested is complete.

Voltmeters

One of the principal uses of a voltmeter [Fig. A-8(a)] is to determine the voltage drop of various elements in a circuit. This, in turn, relates to resistance offered to current flow by each element. To see how a voltage drop test works, suppose that you have examined the connections at the positive terminal of an automobile's battery and found them to be corroded. You wonder if this corrosion might increase resistance enough to create problems (such as reducing current flow to the starter motor and causing hard starting).

To answer your questions, you would set your voltmeter scale on low range so that it will only read a maximum of 2 V. Then you would place one voltmeter lead at the center of the battery's positive terminal and the other voltmeter lead on the battery's positive cable, just beyond the cable clamp. Now you would remove the coil's high-tension wire so that the car can't start and ask someone to turn the ignition switch to the "crank" position. The voltage showing on the voltmeter scale is the voltage drop, the amount of voltage used to

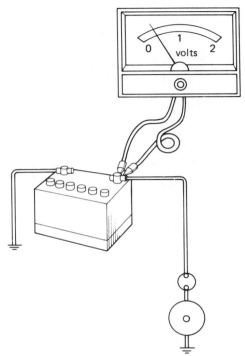

FIG. A-9 Voltage drop test.

push current between the battery's positive terminal and the cable connector. In this case, the voltage drop ought to be 0.1 V or less. If it is more, the cable should be removed and the connection cleaned and examined.

Voltage drop measurements are made with the voltmeter connected parallel to a circuit, with the leads attached on either side of the element being tested (Fig. A-9). That way, some of the current goes through the voltmeter and some goes through the circuit. The voltage reading (looking at it in one way) can be considered the voltage lost or blocked off by the component. In the example above, if the voltage reading were 0.1 V, it would mean (in a 12-V system) that the terminal connections allowed 11.9 V to push through. If the terminal became more corroded, causing the resistance to increase, more voltage would be dropped at the terminal, increasing the voltage reading at the meter.

Ohmmeters

An ohmmeter [Fig. A-8(c)] is used to check the electrical resistance in an electrical component or section of circuit. It is a self-powered device, which means the element tested must be isolated or disconnected from the rest of the circuit. With the ohmmeter leads connected at either end, a known amount of voltage is applied. The amount of current flowing through the meter varies according to the resistance of the device being tested, and hence can be read on the dial of the meter as ohms.

service sampler
B

Battery Testing

This exercise, although not a complete battery test procedure, does outline some quick service and maintenance checks that are widely performed and quite useful.

Warning: Before doing any work around a battery it is very important to remember that a battery is dangerous even if it doesn't appear threatening just sitting there not visibly doing anything. Ask older mechanics. Pretty soon you'll find one who'll tell you what it's like when a battery explodes in an engine compartment. He may even be able to show you some scars. Because of the explosive combination of hydrogen and oxygen gases produced in battery cells, you must never smoke around a battery or cause any sparks. Otherwise, you may have your own scars to show.

VISUAL CHECKS AND CLEANING It is a good idea every now and then to examine a battery for visibly obvious flaws (Fig. B-1) and to clean the case and terminals.

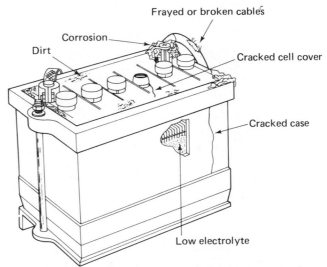

Frayed or broken cables

Corrosion

Dirt

Cracked cell cover

Cracked case

Low electrolyte

FIG. B-1 The external condition of the battery should be checked periodically for damage.

1. Examine the battery's overall appearance. Is the top of the case clean? Are the terminals coated with a caked-on gray deposit? If any of these conditions are present, the battery must be cleaned. Dirt on top of the case can provide a conductive path between the two terminals which will allow the battery to discharge when not in use. Caked-on deposits can increase resistance and diminish the battery's output.

2. To clean the battery case, first make sure that all the filler plugs are in tight so that the cleaning solution will not get into the cells. Then scrub the case with diluted ammonia or with baking soda mixed with water. This will neutralize any acid that may be present. After the battery is clean, flush it off with tap water.

3. If the terminals show any sign of caked-on deposits, first with the cables still attached, clean off as much of the deposit as you can with a wire brush dipped in a soda solution or ammonia. Then remove the cables and clean both the cables and the terminals. When removing the cable clamps, be careful not to damage the terminals. A cable puller may be required if the connections are stuck together. After the cable clamps and terminals have been cleaned and flushed with water, they should be coated with a light coat of petroleum jelly to prevent further corrosion.

4. A battery should be examined for physical defects before and after it is cleaned. Gross defects such as puncture holes or large cracks can be seen, even when the battery is dirty. If the defects are too severe, there is probably no need to clean it in the first place. It should be discarded. Smaller cracks or defects may not be visible until after the battery has been cleaned. A battery may have some service life left, even with small defects. But it should be watched carefully.

5. Remember to handle the battery carefully at all times, both during cleaning and during reinstallation, so as not to break the casing or chip the cell covers.

Service Sampler

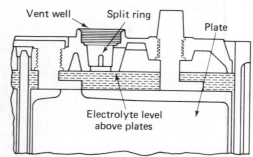

Vent well   Split ring   Plate

Electrolyte level above plates

FIG. B-2 The electrolyte level in the battery (unless it is a sealed unit) should be checked every 2000 miles or once a month.

CHECKING ELECTROLYTE LEVEL

The electrolyte is both a carrier of free electrons between the positive and negative plates and a means for putting the electrons in motion. To do its job it must be at the proper level (Fig. B-2). The tops of the plates must be covered with liquid so that all the plate surface is in action. But the cells shouldn't be overfilled. Otherwise, there will be electrolyte loss and the increased possibility of corrosion.

Some batteries have slit rings at the bottom of the individual cell filler holes. In these batteries, the electrolyte level should be up to the split ring. In other styles of batteries, the level should come to the lower portion of the vent well.

Most manufacturers recommend using distilled water in the battery. However, tap water can be used in areas where the water is "soft" (where it doesn't contain too many mineral deposits).

CHECKING ELECTROLYTE STRENGTH

The strength of the electrolyte is determined with a hydrometer (Fig. B-3), a device for measuring the weight of density of liquids. The more the liquid weighs, the greater the percentage of sulfuric present, and the better the charge in the cell being tested.

To check the specific gravity, first remove the covers from all the cells. Next, put the tip of the hydrometer down into the first cell to be checked, then squeeze the bulb (Fig. B-4). Allow the bulb to slowly expand. As the bulb expands, the electrolyte will be drawn up into the hydrometer tube and the float will begin to rise. Hold the hydrometer in a vertical position so that the float can rise freely.

Read the electrolyte level where it crosses the graduated portion of the float. Make a mental note of the reading, then squeeze the bulb (*while the tip is still in the cell*) to flush the sample from the tube. Go to the next cell and repeat the procedure until all the cells have been checked.

Specific gravity readings will vary according to the temperature. Some hydrometers have built-in means for adjusting the readings according to the temperature. In others, you must do it yourself. If the temperature of the electrolyte is over 80 °F, you must add 0.004 to your original reading for every 10 ° over 80 °F. If the temperature of the electrolyte is under 80 °F, you must subtract 0.004 for every 10 °

FIG. B-3 Hydrometer.

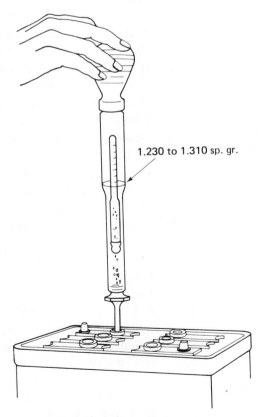

1.230 to 1.310 sp. gr.

FIG. B-4 Using a hydrometer.

under 80 °F. If all the cells read between 1.215 and 1.270 and there is no more than 0.05 difference between the cells, the battery is probably OK. If the cells read below 1.230 but read fairly consistently, a charge may be all that's needed. If the difference between the cells is more than 0.05, the battery is probably defective. If the cells read over 1.270, the electrolyte is overstrength and will probably cause early battery failure.

BATTERY LOAD TEST

The battery load test is a quick way to determine how well a battery performs under actual load conditions. The test device used, called a battery load tester, is produced by most manufacturers of automotive test equipment. Typically, a battery load tester consists of a heavy-duty ammeter, a carbon-pile variable rheostat, and a voltmeter. The ammeter and the rheostat are usually connected to the battery using the same test leads. The voltmeter is connected with its own separate leads.

Before and during the test, these preliminary steps and cautions should be observed:

1. Wear eye protection at all times. Make sure that your work area is well ventilated. Before connecting or disconnecting any alligator clips, be sure that the tester controls are in the OFF position. Make absolutely sure that no arcs or flames are present. Remember that the danger posed by explosive hydrogen gas is very real.
2. Make sure (if possible) that the specific gravity of the electrolyte is at least 1.215 at 80 °F.
3. If a sealed battery is being tested, make sure that the battery is charged. If such a battery has no build-in charge indicator and there is doubt about the state of charge, charge the battery before attempting the load-test.
4. Make sure that the battery temperature is between 70 and 90 °F.
5. Determine the manufacturer's ampere rating of the battery being tested and calculate what three times that rating is.

Following are the steps for performing the load test:

1. Turn the carbon-pile variable rheostat to the OFF position.
2. Connect the heavy-duty tester cables (for the ammeter and rheostat) to the positive and negative terminals of the battery. Connect the red sleeve cable end to the positive terminal and the black sleeve cable end to the negative terminal. Make sure that the alligator clips are securely attached to the battery terminals.
3. Connect the smaller voltmeter leads to the battery, again connecting red to positive and black to negative. At this time, the voltmeter should be reading battery voltage.

4. Slowly turn the rheostat knob in the ON direction. As you do, observe the ammeter reading. When it is three times the battery's ampere rating, stop turning the knob.

5. Hold the knob in this position for 15 seconds. At the end of the 15-second period, quickly observe the voltage reading, then turn the rheostat knob back to the OFF position.

Note: If the reading is less than 9 V for a 12-V battery, the battery is probably defective.

6. After making sure that the carbon pile is in the OFF position, disconnect the tester leads.

C

Starter-System Testing

This exercise describes a series of voltmeter tests that can be used to quickly and simply locate the approximate trouble area in a malfunctioning starter system. These particular directions are for solenoid-operated, overrunning clutch starters; however, they also apply to inertia drive starters controlled by a magnetic switch.

Suppose you have a car that cranks slowly or not at all. You are aware that the problem *could* be caused by:

1. A discharged or weak battery.
2. Very low temperatures.
3. Thick engine oil (which could result from low temperatures).
4. A hot, tight engine.
5. High compression ratios due to deposits accumulated in the combustion chamber.
6. Ignition timing advanced so far that the combustion process tends to push the piston down in the compression stroke.

However, let us also suppose you have already eliminated these conditions as the source of the problem. That leaves the starter motor itself, the starter system wiring, and the solenoid control unit. Since the motor must be removed from the car before it can be thoroughly checked, the best procedure is to first examine the wiring and solenoid switch, which can be tested in place.

To check the wiring and solenoid control, the following tests are performed in the following order. However, before proceeding, the high-tension coil should be removed from the coil so that the car cannot start. Then, someone should hold the ignition switch in the "crank" position while each test is performed.

TEST ONE Connect one voltmeter lead or probe to the center of the positive battery terminal and the other to the battery terminal on the starter solenoid (Fig. C-1). If the voltage drop is 0.2 V or more, there may be excessive resistance in the circuit section you are testing—in other words, between the two terminals where the voltmeter leads are attached. If this is the case, you should check for loose or corroded terminals and damaged or frayed wires.

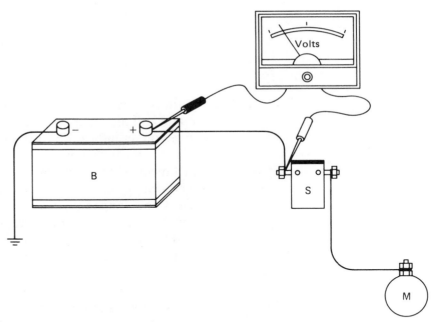

FIG. C-1 Starting-System Test 1.

TEST TWO Connect one voltmeter lead to the solenoid battery terminal and the other to the solenoid motor terminal (Fig. C-2). This voltage drop will give you an indication of the resistance in the high-voltage section of the solenoid (the switch that routes virtually full strength battery current from the battery terminal to the starter motor). If the voltage is 0.2 V or higher, the switch terminals or control plates are probably burned. Depending on the kind of solenoid, the unit would either be repaired or replaced.

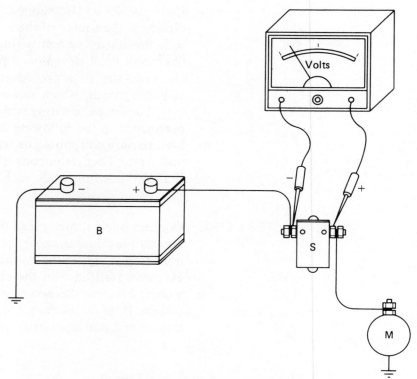

FIG. C-2 Starting-System Test 2.

TEST THREE   Connect one voltmeter lead to the center of the battery negative terminal and the other to the cranking motor frame (Fig. C-3). This will give you an indication of the resistance in the ground return circuit. If the voltage drop is 0.2 V or higher, the cranking motor/engine attachments should be examined for rust or excessive paint. The battery ground connection should also be examined. If you like, you can check the voltage drop at each connection in the ground return circuit by placing the voltmeter leads on either side of the connection points. A rough rule of thumb states that the voltage drop should not exceed 0.1 V at each connection point.

   Note: The three tests just described are usually performed when the solenoid is "pulling in" or working, but the starter motor doesn't turn the engine over, or turns the engine over slowly. The remaining tests are carried out when the solenoid doesn't work at all. However, since none of the tests take very long, it usually is a good idea to perform all of them whenever starter trouble is suspected.

TEST FOUR   Connect one voltmeter lead to the solenoid battery terminal and the other to the solenoid switch terminal (Fig. C-4). This will test the voltage drop or resistance in the solenoid control circuit. If the reading exceeds 2.5 V, you should examine the circuit terminals at the

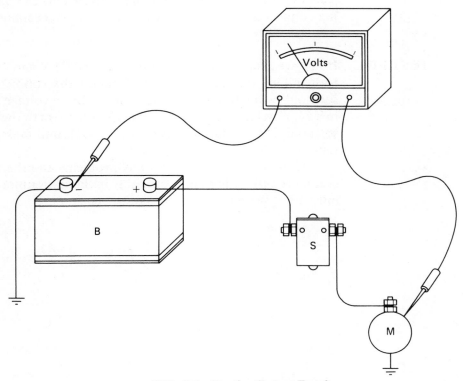

FIG. C-3 Starting-System Test 3.

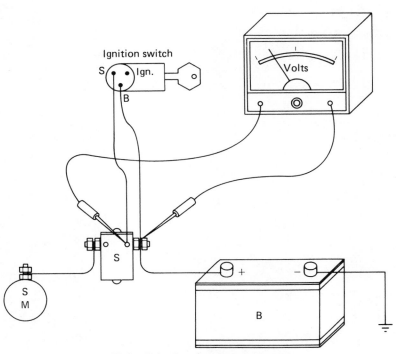

FIG. C-4 Starting-System Test 4.

solenoid, neutral safety switch, ignition switch, and battery. The wiring connecting these terminals should also be examined for damage.

TEST FIVE   If voltage drops in test 4 did not read over 2.5 V and the solenoid still isn't pulling in, perform test 5. Connect the voltmeter leads to the solenoid switch terminal and to ground. If the voltage is at least 7.7 V in a 12-V system, the solenoid doesn't feel warm to the touch, and the solenoid doesn't pull in, the unit is at fault and must be repaired or replaced.

If these tests fail to show any problems and the car still fails to crank properly, the fault is probably in the starter motor itself, which must be removed and tested on the bench.

service sampler
D

Charging-System Testing

Charging-system service is a specialized job often carried out in automotive electrical shops that deal exclusively with testing and repairing starter motors, generators, and alternators. Such service techniques are beyond the scope of this exercise section. However, there are a few quick checks and tests that will let you determine if a problem is due to a malfunction in the charging system.

Usually, the first indication of a charging-system problem is poor battery performance. Either the battery will be overcharged and using too much water (possibly fuses will burn out frequently), or the battery will be undercharged and the car will be difficult to start. Such difficulties *could* be the result of a malfunctioning charging system. They could also be due to a bad battery or defective wiring. So before examining the alternator or generator, it is important to eliminate these other factors as possible causes of the trouble. A load test should be performed on the battery and the wiring and terminal connectors should be examined. Also, if the battery is undercharged, the alternator drive belt should be checked to see if it is installed at the proper tension and if it is in good shape.

If, after everything else has been examined and put in good order, the battery (which has been proved to be otherwise sound) still shows signs of overcharging or undercharging, the problem is likely to be in the charging system itself. A variety of alternator test procedures are available for different makes of vehicles. Following are two typical examples.

GENERATOR/ ALTERNATOR OUTPUT TEST

(Fig. D-1). Perform these steps:

1. Disconnect the battery ground cable.
2. Disconnect the red wire from the BAT terminal on the alternator.
3. Connect an ammeter black lead (negative) to the red wire and the ammeter red lead (positive) to the BAT terminal on the alternator.
4. Reconnect the battery ground cable.
5. Turn on all the accessories, the windshield wipers, and the hazard warning lamps. Turn the headlights on high beam and the fan blower on high speed. If the battery is fully charged, use the starter to partially discharge it.
6. Run the engine just fast enough to obtain the maximum current reading on the ammeter.
7. If the current reading is within 10 A of the rated output of the alternator, the reading is normal.
8. If the current is not within 10 A of the rated output, continue the test: Insert a screwdriver into the test hole at the end of the alternator frame. The screwdriver should touch the tab in the test hole and should be grounded against the side of the hole.
9. If the reading is now within 10 A of the rated output, the regulator is defective and should be replaced. If the rating is not within 10 A of the rated output, the alternator is defective and must be removed for internal testing and inspection.

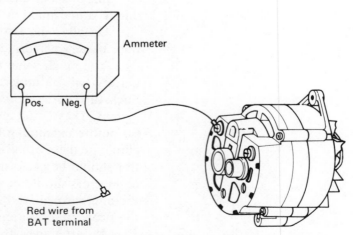

FIG. D-1 Check the generator output with engine running and all lights and accessories on.

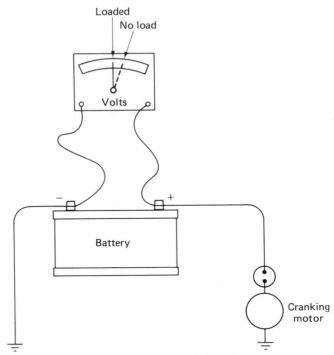

FIG. D-2 No load/load test.

NO LOAD/LOAD TEST (Fig. D-2). Perform these steps:

1. Connect the negative lead of a voltmeter to the battery's negative cable clamp.
2. Connect the positive voltmeter lead to the battery's positive cable clamp.
3. Record the battery voltage shown in the voltmeter scale. This is called the base voltage.
4. Connect a tachometer to the engine.
5. Start the engine and increase the speed to 1500 r/min.
6. With no electrical load on the engine (foot off the brake and all doors closed), the voltage reading should increase, but not more than 2 V above the base voltage. It may take a couple of minutes to reach this maximum, whatever it is.
7. Increase the electrical load by turning the headlights on high beam and the fan blower to the high position.
8. Increase the engine speed to 2000 r/min.
9. The voltage should rise again, but this time no more than 0.5 V above the base voltage.

If both of these test results were satisfactory, the charging system is OK.

service sampler

E

Ignition-System Testing

Normally, ignition-system service is conducted at regular intervals during the tune-up procedure, whether or not any trouble is indicated. The following exercise will lead you through a simple troubleshooting procedure that can be used when there *is* something wrong.

As in all electrical-system testing, the first item checked is the battery. It is the heart of all electrical system components. So if you have a car that runs poorly or not at all, a load test should be performed to see if the battery is OK. A discharged battery can cause ignition problems, particularly during cranking. It may not have enough power to both turn the engine over and provide a spark.

After the battery has been found to be satisfactory (or made to be all right, and assuming that the car still doesn't run or runs poorly), the next step is to find out if the problem is in the ignition system as a whole. There are two general ways to tell.

CONDITION A Using a pair of insulated pliers, hold the metal end of a spark plug cable ¼ inch from ground while the engine is cranking. (If the cable end is covered with a rubber booth, you may have to insert a spark plug in the boot, ground the tip of the plug, and observe the gap.) If a spark is visible, the ignition system should be functioning well enough for the engine to run (although the dwell and timing *could* be drastically off). If there isn't a spark, the ignition system is not working at all. For the purposes of this procedure, we will refer to such a no-spark condition as condition A.

CONDITION B   If the car starts but stops as soon as the ignition switch is released, the problem is likely in the ignition system. We will call this condition B.

TESTING FOR CONDITION A   If no spark occurs at the spark plug, the next step is to determine if the problem is in the primary or secondary circuits. To to this, pull the high-tension lead from the coil to the distributor loose at the distributor and hold the metal end ¼ inch from ground (Fig. E-1). If a spark is present, you will know that the high-voltage surge is arriving at the distributor but that it is not (from the previous test) reaching the spark plug. So the trouble has to be somewhere in the distributor secondary circuit (cap and rotor button) or in the spark plug wires. However, if no spark is present, you could assume that the problem is in the primary circuit.

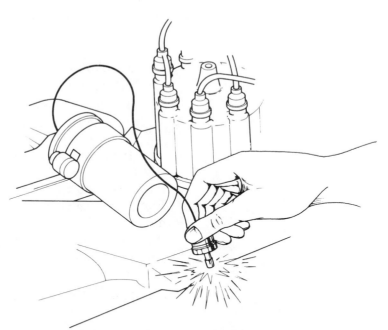

FIG. E-1   Checking coil secondary output.

As shown in Fig. E-2, the primary circuit is checked first by connecting voltmeter leads to the positive battery terminal and to the positive terminal on the coil (the terminal connected to the small wire going back to the ignition switch or wiring harness, *not* the small wire going to the distributor). The voltage reading, while the engine is cranking, should be less than 1.0 V. If it isn't, one or more of these conditions might be present:

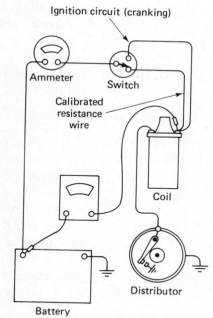

FIG. E-2 Primary circuit test: First check.

1. An open circuit between battery and battery side of coil.
2. Ignition switch not closing.
3. A ground condition in the ignition bypass circuit between the coil and the battery.

If the previous test read less than 1.0 V and condition A were still present, the next test should be carried out. Remove the distributor cap and rotor but leave all the primary connections attached. Bump the engine over until the points are open. Connect the voltmeter leads to the coil's positive terminal and to ground, (Fig. E-3). With the ignition switch on, you should read full battery voltage. If you don't, one of these conditions might be present:

1. An open condition in the circuit from the coil to the distributor.
2. An open condition in the ignition circuit used during cranking.
3. An open circuit in the resistance lead.

TESTING FOR CONDITION B If the initial examination showed that the car would start but then stop immediately after the ignition key was released from the crank position, the following test would be in order: Using a test lead with alligator clips at both ends, connect one clip to the coil's negative (distributor) terminal and the other clip to a clean point on the mass

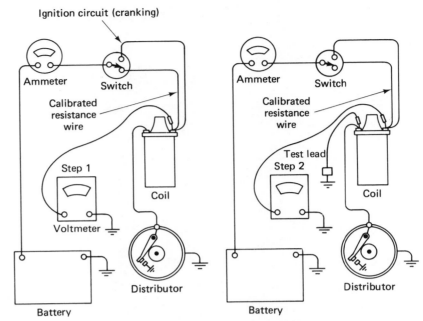

FIG. E-3 Primary circuit test: Second check.

of the engine. This will ground the coil's primary lead. Next, attach a voltmeter's positive lead to the coil's positive (ignition) terminal and the voltmeter's negative lead to ground (Fig. E-3). Turn the ignition switch to the ON position. The meter should read between 4 and 8 on a car with a 12-V ignition system. If it doesn't, check for the following conditions:

1. An open resistor in the ignition circuit.
2. A defective ignition switch.
3. An open circuit between the resistor and the ignition switch.

Index